A Manual of
Steam Locomotive
Restoration and Preservation

D. W. Harvey

DAVID & CHARLES
Newton Abbot London North Pomfret (Vt)

British Library Cataloguing in Publication Data

Harvey, D. W.
  A manual of steam locomotive restoration and
  preservation.
  1. Locomotives–Conservation and restoration
  I. Title
  625.2'61   TJ608

  ISBN 0-7153-7770-1

Library of Congress Catalog Card Number 79–56051

First published 1980
Second impression 1980
Third impression 1981

Printed in Great Britain by
Biddles Limited, Guildford
for David & Charles (Publishers) Limited
Brunel House, Newton Abbot, Devon

Published in the United States of America
by David & Charles Inc.
North Pomfret, Vermont 05053 USA

Contents

CONTENTS *(continued)*

Author's Note and Acknowledgements

Dr Peter Beet of 'Steamtown', Carnforth, first suggested that I should record what experience and 'know how' I have gained during half a century of maintaining and running steam railway locomotives. This practical manual is the result of that suggestion.

For the past twenty eight years, most of my leisure time has been devoted to the preservation and restoration of steam locomotives both large and small, and if the information I have set down in this treatise helps others to prolong the working life of a machine that has fascinated and captivated so many generations I shall feel amply rewarded.

I would like to acknowledge the help and advice I have received from various friends and colleagues, in particular John Bellwood, CME of the National Railway Museum, John Brown of HM Railway Inspectorate, Department of Transport, Allan Garraway and David Madden, General Managers of the Festiniog and North Norfolk railways respectively, and David Morgan, my legal adviser.

My grateful thanks are also due to Arnold Hoskins, the Leicester Mercury, Major P. Olver of HM Railway Inspectorate, Dr Coiley and his staff of the National Railway Museum for permission to reproduce many of the rare photographs that illustrate this book, John Edgington for the photographs of the sectioned Merchant Navy class locomotive, David Ward of British Rail for his all round encouragement and to R. H. N. Hardy, Executive Member, Central Engineering Training Group, BRB.

Lastly I am indebted to the three charming women who have helped me so much, my agent and editor Eileen da Silva, and Margaret Ritchie and Joanne James with their help in typing and proof reading.

D. W. HARVEY MIMechE
July 1979

PUBLISHER'S NOTE The drawings in this book were specially prepared by the author. Photographs credited to the National Railway Museum are Crown Copyright and reproduced by permission of the Keeper.

The author at his desk. (*Eastern Evening News*)

Foreword

To read David William Harvey on railway matters is always an education but this book is additionally fascinating because it is a much needed textbook of a type that had to be written sooner or later by a man of experience for people involved in the maintenance and repair of preserved steam locomotives.

When that man of experience is the remarkable D. W. Harvey who has a certain simple mastery of the written word and who also happens to be one of the finest practical steam locomotive engineers of recent times, the book is of immediate value to those who want to know how it should be done.

To write the foreword is a pleasure for I have known the author for thirty three out of my thirty eight years with the LNER and BR. Nearly every page brings to mind some incident experienced, some remarkable men with whom I have worked, but the book also recreates in my mind photographs galore of David Harvey in action and what he can do; so can other people if they try hard enough.

Of course, my old friend and I are very different. He has never cut corners in his life; to him, to maintain the steam locomotive was to seek and to find perfection, whereas I, after several years of steam traction at Stratford, had become educated in the arts of survival, compromise, expediency and the taking of personal risks. It has been said that Stratford, the great leveller, would have levelled David Harvey. This is open to doubt but there would have been a volcanic, not to say titanic struggle. We can never say for sure for he wisely preferred the comparatively cloistered calm of Norwich in which to work his magic. Nevertheless, some time in the late 1940s, Neasden Depot needed revitalising and he was sent there for several months. The state of maintenance was low but, slowly and surely, conditions began to improve and when he returned to Norwich, his purpose served, he received a letter from the enginemen's LDC, congratulating him on what had been achieved. Over the years, one occasionally receives such letters from men to whom writing does not necessarily come easily and to whom it comes even harder to express a written compliment to management, and I can understand the sense of pride with which he retains this genuine, sincere and friendly letter, to this day.

The book opens with a chapter on 'Safety First'. On reading it, you realise that you have taken needless risks. To work on and maintain locomotives which can and will move, needs clear headed concentration, not just instinct and experience. I was reminded of the H class tank that moved gently down the yard at Stewarts Lane one winter evening in 1954, colliding with an incoming King Arthur, to the combined profanity of driver, fireman and foreman, vented upon an empty cab. Who omitted to obey the simple rules, we never did find out!

In this book common-sense and first principles are found yet it also highlights the extraordinary blend of craftsmanship and knowledge with hard, rough, dirty, thoroughly unpleasant work, required to maintain the steam locomotive in permanent and intensive service. The steam locomotives of today are well cared for by people who do the work largely because they want to do it. Generally, they can take their time; not for them the continuous oppression of the timetable, the requirements of the Running Foreman, the tyranny of washing out locomotive boilers for a living in an open ended, dark, bitterly cold, smoke-choked depot where work was sometimes skimped, or a washout plug found with only one turn of the thread in the firebox faceplate under 200 lb per square inch of steam.

And yet, the right way can still become the wrong way through inexperience or lack of understanding and knowledge. Every word in this book is recommended to those involved in present day steam locomotive maintenance; every sentence carries practical, sensible advice, for the author, whatever we thought of Norwich when I was in charge of Ipswich Depot, came as near to the perfection of steam locomotive maintenance as has been possible in the post war world of main line railway work in this country. He always found time to find the reason why and then to work out a remedy. It is for the people who, under present conditions, take up the same sort of challenge, that he has written this book.

Amersham   R. H. N. HARDY

Buckinghamshire   CEng, FIMechE

The cut-away rebuilt Bulleid Merchant Navy 4-6-2 No 35029 *Ellerman Line*, now part of the National collection housed at the National Railway Museum at York. The locomotive has not been cut away into even halves but to the best advantage to show the major features impossible to see in a normal complete locomotive. *Above* is the engine looking towards the back and, *below*, a side view showing the detail of the firebox and thermic syphon. (*J. Edgington*)

Safety First

'Any fool can learn in a few seconds how to start a steam locomotive, but in certain conditions even a skilled man with a lifetime's experience cannot stop one!' This is the time honoured advice given to beginners.

OVERFILLING THE BOILER

Hydraulicing or the carry over of water into the cylinder from a boiler that has been overfilled is a most dangerous condition. Once an engine, especially a superheater engine, has 'got hold of the water' it cannot be stopped because the water flashes instantly into steam. Hydraulicing is frequently accompanied by violent and prolonged slipping with the risk of smashing cylinders and covers or buckling connecting rod and coupling rods.

Should the engine not slip it will career out of control even though the regulator has been closed, the brake applied and cylinder drain cocks opened until the water charged steam circuit has been exhausted or the driver has succeeded in reversing the engine.

The moral of this is not to overfill the boiler, especially when there is a tendency to prime or foam. The water level should be kept well in sight always, preferably not more than half or two thirds of a glassfull.

BLOWBACKS

Do not turn the firebox into a gas retort by cramming it full of coal up to the level of the brick arch so depriving the fire of air by closing the firedoor and dampers. The gases released when the fire is subsequently stirred with the pricker are liable to explode and fill the cab with a sheet of flame which can be quite frightening. It will undoubtedly singe your whiskers!

There is another kind of blowback that can occur on the road but this can be guarded against. It is encountered when entering a tunnel, especially one of single bore, by the air displaced on impact causing an up draught through the ashpan and a down draught through the chimney, which is exaggerated if the regulator is closed or partially closed.

Anticipate this contingency by closing the dampers and firedoor and putting the blower hard on when approaching a tunnel. Neglect of these precautions in the past has led to the crew being terribly burnt when the outburst of flame has been so sustained that the coal in the tender has started to ignite.

LOW STEAM PRESSURE AND INADEQUATE BRAKE POWER

Moving engines low in steam with insufficient pressure to operate the power brake can also be hazardous. Make sure that the steam pressure is high enough to operate the brakes *before* an engine is moved.

STOP BOARDS

Before moving an engine, operating an injector, or reversing the valve gear etc, first make sure that there is no one working under or about the engine. Also shout a warning such as 'Stand clear (of) 4472!' or 'Look out for injector (or lever or cylinder cocks) 4073!'

Men working on other engines on the same road should also be warned to stand clear in case of accidental collision. Many a poor fellow while underneath, oiling a crank shaft of an inside cylinder engine, has been crushed to death through neglect of these elementary precautions.

Those working on an engine also have a responsibility to protect themselves by placing a stop board marked NOT TO BE MOVED on the regulator handle or a red flag on each side of the engine before going underneath. If the engine is in steam, also warn the engine crew or you may be subjected to a shower of red hot cinders when the fire is stirred, or scalded with hot water when the water level in the boiler is tested.

Similarly two red lights should be displayed after dark facing the direction from which shunting movements can be made. It is a criminal offence to remove these or the stop boards without the consent of the person who placed them.

The golden rule when leaving an engine in steam unattended is:

1. Shut the regulator.
2. Apply the brake (power and hand).
3. Put the reverser in mid-gear.
4. Open the cylinder drain cocks.
5. Scotch the driving wheels.

Even if the regulator does blow through, an engine will not move if these precautions are taken. Likewise do not forget to close the regulator of a dead engine after filling the boiler; cases of engines moving of their own accord when sufficient steam pressure has been generated are not unknown.

Other 'don'ts' for your personal safety are:

Don't pass between buffers when they are at all close, and certainly not when shunting is going on in the vicinity.
Don't leap or stride across pits. Their edges are often greasy and a slip could mean broken ribs. Walk around or cross a footplate, even if it does take longer.
Don't open the blower when your mate is cleaning out the smokebox, without first warning him; he could be scalded!

SAFETY IN SHEDS AND WORKSHOP

Keep the shed and machine shop floor clean and clear of obstacles to trip over, or oily patches to slip on.

In the machine shop see that guards are provided (and used) for moving parts where the operator is liable to be caught up in the machinery. This is a requirement under the Health & Safety at Work Act, the provisions of which cover safe practices in workshops and elsewhere.

For the same reason do not wear loose clothing or too long hair, and if you must use a file on work in the lathe, use it *left* handed.

When using a tool grinder, see that the rest is set close to the wheel, and wear goggles.

Do *not* use the stone for grinding aluminium – it ruins the wheel and when subsequently used for grinding steel there is a tendency for this to 'pick-up' or adhere and be jerked out of the hands.

Never, when putting up motion or similar parts, use a finger to test the alignment of holes; a heavy expansion link or bearing spring is a first

class guillotine and could make a neat amputation.

Do *not* use the tang of a file as a pin punch – the end struck by the hammer is glass hard and a flake may fly off and injure an eye.

Do *not* use a file without a handle or with a handle that is a loose fit; should it slip out of the hand giving the thrust, when the other hand is exerting a downward pressure, the tang end may well fly up and pierce an eye.

The correct method of holding a file is to grasp the handle with the fingers and thumb with the rounded end in the centre of the palm, so that the file becomes in effect an extension of the forearm. Both thrust and pressure, so necessary for filing flat, are better controlled in this way than by holding it like a barrow handle.

Do *not* use a hammer with a loose head – a flying hammer head can easily stun a man or perhaps worse.

See that hammer wedges are secure and occasionally stand the hammer in a bucket of water overnight to swell the wood.

When striking a chisel bar or punch bar with a long shafted heavy hammer, see that your mate who is holding the bar, stands facing you; he should *never* stand at your side for should you miss the bar he will receive the full force of the blow, possibly in the face.

When chipping at the bench or turning brass in a lathe, erect a screen of some kind behind the work to prevent the needle sharp chips flying into the face and eyes of any workmate.

When using a hammer and chisel, watch the cutting edge and not the head if you wish to avoid bruised and bleeding knuckles.

For the same reason relax the muscles of the thumb and fore-finger; should you miss the chisel, the blow is less painful than if the muscles are tense.

At the end of a cut or if the chisel is not held at the correct cutting angle it is liable to be knocked from between the fingers, therefore the rags or burrs that form at the head should be ground off to prevent the flesh from being lacerated.

Do *not* show how strong you are by lifting or carrying bodily too heavy an article; always halve the load to be raised by lifting one end only at a time. Suppose for example you wish to move or raise a heavy tool chest weighing perhaps 2 cwt; lift one end and using the opposite corner as a pivot, swing the chest round through 180°, lower it and repeat from the opposite end and so on.

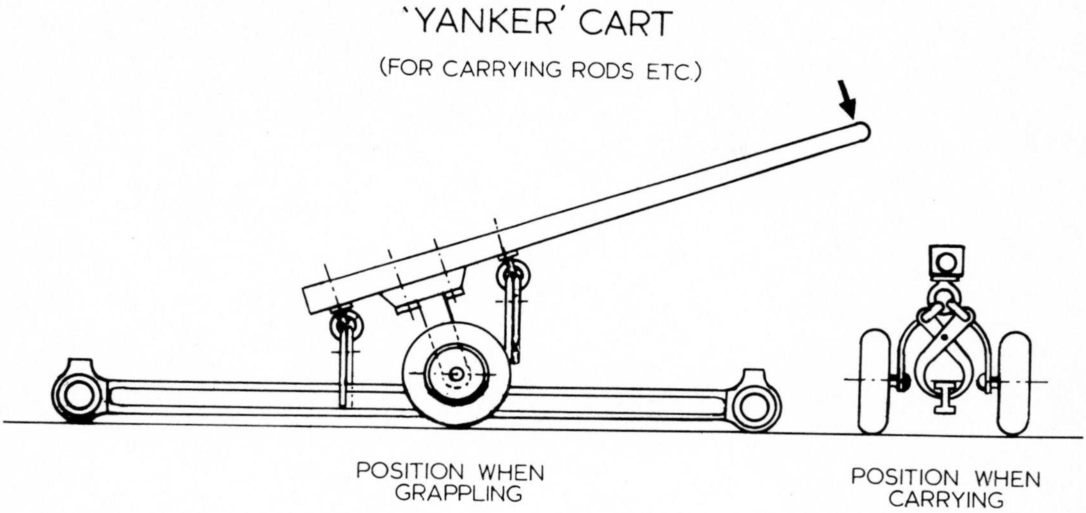

'YANKER' CART

(FOR CARRYING RODS ETC.)

POSITION WHEN
GRAPPLING

POSITION WHEN
CARRYING

Fig 1. A 'yanker' cart with grappling arms for carrying rods and other long heavy components. The long arm gives adequate purchase to raise coupling rods clear of the ground, and, when both grappling irons are engaged, the weight of the rod, if mounted centrally, will be supported evenly on both sides of the wheels.

Heavy inside connecting rods were 'walked' about the shop in this way, by standing them upright and then alternately rocking and swinging them from corner to corner on their butt ends.

In a like manner use the article itself as a lever when lifting, by slipping a wedge or packing of increasing thickness under the end raised in order to gain height and then repeat from the opposite end.

The principles of the lever, roller and wedge are just as valid today as when the ancient Egyptians built their Pyramids. Use them; it is brain not brawn that wins in the long run.

Crippling hernias and slipped discs can all too easily result from using the human spine as a crane. Lift with the feet together and the back and arms straight, using the knees and the powerful muscles of the legs to do the lifting in exactly the same way as an experienced oarsman propels a sculling boat or racing eight.

Do *not* use oil or grease on the screwed connections of oxygen or acetylene cylinders. This has been known to cause spontaneous combustion; non-return valves are fitted to hoses for this reason. Whenever possible, stand the cylinders upright.

Do *not* use frayed or knotted rope of dubious strength for lifting heavy items.

When annealing copper pipes do *not* plunge the red hot end into water for there will be an instant generation of steam and you may sustain a badly scalded face from the resulting geyser. If the pipe cannot be wholly immersed, then pour water over its outside.

Ladders

In order to prevent a ladder slipping from under you on a greasy floor, sprinkle the floor with sand and stand the ladder on a dry cloth, also incline it as steeply as possible; if it can be tied by one of its rungs to the engine handrail so much the better – and safer. Make sure that the ladder you are about to use is sound and has neither split nor broken rails, nor loose or missing rungs.

On open days or other occasions when the public are invited on to the footplate, caution them to face inwards when descending from the engine footsteps. It is truly remarkable how many people attempt to do so facing outwards, who would never think of descending a ladder in that fashion.

Servicing

In the days when steam traction was all but universal, locomotives were worked hard; some passenger classes achieved more than 10,000 miles a month and all were expected to be available for traffic for eighty-five days out of every one hundred. Overhauls in Main Works, repairs and examination at Running Sheds and periodic washing out of boilers accounted for the remaining fifteen days.

Today our preserved steam locomotives, unless operating regularly on a privately owned railway, spend far more time out of service than running and never again are we likely to see engines coming on the shed with smokeboxes filled with char up to the level of the crossbar. The maintenance problems are consequently very different and rust rather than wear is probably the biggest enemy.

British Railways' schedule of standard examinations for steam locomotives, MP11, is based on mileage run in normal everyday service and this fact must be taken into account when applying that schedule to locomotives that work only occasionally. Regular and thorough inspection of an engine whenever it is steamed and prompt attention given to any defects found, will however help to keep it in a good and safe condition.

INSPECTION AND SERVICING

The best time to examine an engine for defects is immediately on arrival at the Shed before bearings have had time to cool down, or the crew have left.

REPORTING OF DEFECTS

In the days of steam on British Rail it was the driver's responsibility on arrival at the shed to record in a repair book or on a card any defects noticed during the journey, or found during examination of the engine. Today when preserved steam locomotives are worked on BR lines by BR crews, this requirement no longer applies; it is therefore essential that the driver should be questioned as to any known defects before he leaves the engine and these should be recorded. A chalked 'X' on a blowing pipe union or steam joint is an easy and certain method of identifying a blow.

A common failing among drivers is a tendency to prescribe the remedy rather than to describe the symptom when reporting a defect. This can be particularly baffling with the injector or automatic brake defects where there can be a variety of reasons for their non-function.

'Injector to clean out' might or might not effect a cure, but it is not very helpful in arriving at the cause. Likewise one is left guessing as to why an engine is reported as 'not good enough for main line'. Much time and unnecessary work by repair staff can be avoided therefore by a clear understanding of exactly what the driver experienced.

MECHANICAL EXAMINATION

A methodical inspection of the engine should be made next, starting at the front on one side, proceeding to the rear of the engine or tender and returning along the opposite side before finally going underneath. The temperature of the axleboxes, coupling rod and connecting rod bearings should be felt with the back of the hand, the temperature of these parts should not be above blood heat and they frequently run stone cold. The presence of a grey paste or brass dust on wheel spokes is a sure indication of heating and if removable oil trays or 'keeps' are fitted, they should be withdrawn for inspection. The presence of molten metal on an axle pad will indicate the desirability of immediately dropping the wheels for further inspection.

When going around and underneath the engine a close search should be made for fractures and loose or displaced parts, especially spring plates which may have shifted in the buckle or have fractured near the ends of those plates attached to the spring hangers.

Flaw detection

It is sometimes difficult to distinguish between

Regular cleaning of tubes is an essential part of steam locomotive servicing. Condensation, combined with unswept tubes, on an engine used infrequently can soon lead to corrosion. Great Western engines such as No

4555 of the Dart Valley Railway are equipped with a steam valve in the smokebox to allow cleaning with a steam lance.
(J. R. Besley, courtesy Dart Valley Railway)

a scratch and a hair-line crack. When in doubt clean the suspected area well with paraffin, spray with flaw detector fluid (alternatively give a very thin coat of limewash), allow to dry thoroughly and strike smartly with a hammer near to the treated area. If a crack exists oil will exude from it discolouring the prepared surface.

Tyres and axles

Tyres should ring true when struck with a hammer; this, however, is not infallible. A dull note will be emitted if, for instance, vibrations are dampened by a brake block touching the tyre.

A visual examination is generally more reliable. Suspect looseness if there is a break in the fillet of dirt where the tyre is shrunk on to the wheel centre. Similarly a break in the paint covering an axle end, or in the webs of a built up crank axle, indicates that these parts are beginning to 'work', especially if the oil exuding from the crack is of a reddish colour – a sure sign that fretting corrosion is occurring.

Tyre flanges wearing thin and sharp should also be looked for and checked by profile gauge as these can cause derailment by splitting facing points or climbing the rails; $\frac{5}{16}$ inch is the minimum safe radius on the edge of a flange. The advice of BR should be sought in such cases and a close watch kept for further deterioration.

Loose fastenings

Split cotters and split pins should fit closely to the nuts or parts they are intended to stop from loosening, otherwise they become necked and liable to break. Nuts and big end cotters should be washered or shimmed up accordingly.

Broken and leaking pipes

The condition of the flexible connection between engine and tender ie, injector feed and brake hoses should also be noted, likewise drawbar springs and pins. Look especially for bent or broken oil pipes feeding axleboxes, leaking unions, chafed oil pipes and loose clips and see that they are rectified; it may avert a hot box.

DISPOSAL

The mechanical condition of the engine and tender having been established the disposal of the engine can now proceed in this order:
1. Smokebox.
2. Firebox.
3. Ashpan.

It is customary to put the blower hard on while the contents of the smokebox are being shovelled out in order to carry away dust and fumes, and it is bad practice to throw out the fire before emptying the smokebox as by so doing cold air is drawn straight into the still hot tubes and firebox stays causing them to contract and leak.

Examination of smokebox

On opening the smokebox door and before commencing disposal, a careful search should be made for any signs of air leaks or steam blows. If below the ash line, the former are generally betrayed by the ashes having ignited where the air is entering and causing local over-heating of the smokebox plates.

If above the ash level, there will be no such tell-tale indication and therefore a very careful scrutiny of the exterior of the smokebox, particularly round the base of the snifting valves, if so fitted, is necessary, as these are very difficult to keep airtight.

Steam blows

Disturbance of the smokebox char or ashes is a clear indication of a blow, but it does not necessarily follow that the defective joint is where the ashes have been blown away. A badly blowing superheater element joint has sometimes directed a jet of steam downwards to disturb the char at the bottom of the smokebox.

The normal internal appearance of a smokebox is a dull grey, but if, for instance, a pipe union has been blowing, there will be a 'vee' shaped bright black mark along the pipe where the jet of steam has scoured away the soot.

All the internal steam fittings should be tried in turn, including opening the regulator, after securing the engine and putting it out of gear in order to test the steam pipes and elements.

Sometimes a steam blow can be seen, sometimes not, but it can be heard and searching the smokebox with a flare lamp is a good method of locating it, as the flame will be deflected or extinguished when brought into the vicinity of the blow. Even this method fails on occasion and then it is necessary to resort to the hydraulic method of testing which will be described in detail later.

Firebars

These should be examined and any warped or broken bars replaced, and any clinker, sealing the air spaces between the bars, removed with a chipping hammer.

It is good practice, for two reasons, occasionally to lift out a few of the side bars in a wide firebox and some of the back bars in a narrow firebox engine to make sure that ash has not accumulated in the shallow part of the ashpan. Firstly, steaming is likely to be affected by a restricted air supply and secondly, if there is not a current of air to keep the bars relatively cool, they will melt and collapse, perhaps also burning the steel carrier bar which is often difficult to replace.

Most modern engines are fitted with rocking grates, some with sections cast in one piece like a grating and others with individual segments threaded on a carrier bar resembling a piece of bullhead rail. This latter variety is the original American 'Hulsen' grate and can be recognised by its corrugated surface.

There are small air ports or holes in the flanks of the corrugations and they are particularly liable to become blocked with fused clinker. Cleaning out these numerous ports with a hammer and punch is a tedious but necessary task.

Brick arch

While in the firebox the condition of the brick arch should be inspected, *especially the side bricks that rest on the carrier bars supporting the arch.* Fracture of these bricks is difficult to repair and frequently leads to the collapse of a complete course or row.

Firebox tube plate

Before tube cleaning, the 'birds nest' on the firebox tube plate should be removed, also the adhesions on the roof stays. This is done by means of a small rake or scraper, the handle of which is turned over at the end and inserted into the tube and the 'birds nest' or fused clinker hooked out. The brick arch is also raked down, for the bottom row or two of the tubes are frequently completely blocked with fine ash.

TUBE CLEANING

Regular and thorough cleaning of tubes, flues, firebox, firebox tube plate, smokebox and ashpan, besides promoting free steaming, will go a long way towards prolonging the life of these components. Wastage by corrosion of the smokebox tube plate and adjacent steam pipes will also be reduced by the elimination of ash and moisture. There are several ways of cleaning tubes:

The steam lance

Many LMS engines and all GWR and BR engines are equipped with a steam valve at the right hand side of the smokebox front plate, to which is connected a flexible hose terminating in a lance, so that tubes and flues can be cleaned from the steam supply while the engine is still in steam.

The compressed air lance

A similar method was used substituting compressed air for steam for engines equipped with the Westinghouse air brake. It can also be connected to a compressed air main.

Tube rod and spun yarn

This is probably the most effective – although certainly the dirtiest and most laborious of the three methods. It consists of a rod of $\frac{3}{8}$ inch steel wire, long enough for an operator standing in front of the smokebox, to penetrate the firebox tube plate with it. One end has a loop handle and the other a needle eye through which is inserted a hank of spun yarn. Care is necessary to see that the plug or mop so formed does not fit the tube too tightly or, on reaching the firebox end, it will not pass the reduced section where the tube is swaged down, and often, on attempting to withdraw it, it will double back on itself and jam solid. Piecemeal removal of the spun yarn from the firebox end is then the only remedy.

A tube rod is not very effective in cleaning superheater flues owing to the presence of the elements. The rod should be used without spun yarn in order to make a way through the ash or clinker and the deposit flushed out with a jet of high pressure water from a lance connected to a boiler wash-out hose, but not of course when the boiler is hot. If tubes are cleaned frequently and thoroughly by steam or compressed air, such drastic measures should not be necessary.

STALE COAL

Before replenishing the tender or bunker, pull forward all the stale coal that tends to accumulate at the back and burn it on shed duties. This will ensure that there is a good coal left when it is most needed, at the end of a long run when the fire is getting clinkered and the fireman tired, besides sparing the owner the humiliation of the engine he has so carefully prepared in all other respects, losing time.

Coal dumps

Although strictly speaking not connected with servicing, it is also a good plan before dumping coal on the ground, to make a hard surface of old steel plate from which to shovel and thus prevent ballast, earth and other incombustible matter from finding its way into the tender when the dump is picked up.

SECTION III
Boiler

BOILER REPAIRS

A steam boiler in certain circumstances is potentially a steam bomb and the effect of any explosion can be almost as devastating as high explosive. It is for this reason that the Board of Trade, the Department of Transport and other responsible authorities insist on the highest standards of maintenance and repair by qualified staff.

Qualified Boilersmith to oversee work

A recent unfortunate incident has caused these already stringent regulations to be tightened even further and now **no repair of any consequence including welding may be carried out except by, or under, the supervision of a qualified boilersmith or boiler inspector.**

This being so, the scope for undertaking boiler repairs even by the most skilled amateurs will be limited in future to retubing the small, plain smoke tubes.

In steam days the tuber was classed as semi-skilled and even during the second world war was never up-graded, such are the special skills required by the boilersmith in detecting and renewing broken stays, patching of seams etc, whereas his counterpart on the fitting side, the steam jointmaker was often up-graded to 'Fitter' for the duration of the war.

Corrosion

The sulphurous products of combustion when damp are extremely corrosive, boiler tubes being especially vulnerable. Besides being relatively thin, they are subject to attack both from inside

16

Left: Boiler failure resulting in explosion has the effect of a bomb, and can cause serious injury, even fatalities, and severe damage. This was a boiler explosion on the Caledonian Railway at Bridge of Dun in March 1872. (*H.M. Railway Inspectorate*)

Right: The effect of internal and external corrosion on a blocked boiler tube. (*National Railway Museum*)

Below: An example of severe local pitting on a boiler tube. (*National Railway Museum*)

and outside, from the out, or water side, because of electrolytic action between copper and steel and internally from the corrosive effect with sulphur and moisture, plus the cutting action of cinders drawn through by blast. It was common experience that engines when put back into service after storage frequently sustained perforated tubes.

A perforated tube, although alarming and filling the cab with steam, is not generally dangerous. However, one that has been reduced to paper thinness through local corrosion just inside the tube plate and has broken, will allow the contents of the boiler to discharge full bore into the firebox and flash instantly into steam — with disastrous consequences. It is for this reason that on many Continental railways, a self-closing firedoor is obligatory, to safeguard the crew in the event of such a catastrophe.

TUBE RENEWAL

Tube expanders for both firebox and smokebox ends, preferably of the five roller water side type will be required. Also a hand hammer and flat chisel for chipping off the beadings, and a 'ripping' tool (resembling a cross cut chisel) for slitting and collapsing the tube for renewal.

Usually, once a tube has been collapsed at the firebox end it can be driven out with a drift and 7lb hammer, but should it prove very stubborn, slitting at the smokebox end may also be necessary but not of course with a torch, on account of the risk of damaging the steel tube plate. A tapered drift and beading tool will also be required for securing and beading the new tube.

A forge, anvil and swage blocks for reducing the diameter at the firebox end will be needed too in case the new tubes are slightly too large in diameter to enter the holes in the copper tubeplate.

Care and the skill that comes with practice are the principal ingredients for success, especially when using the ripping tool. It is all too easy to 'keyhole' or cut a groove in the soft copper of the tube plate when attempting to slit the tube. This risk is avoided if an oxy-acetylene cutting torch is used to slit the tube.

In bad cases, where the groove penetrates to the water side of the tube, it may be necessary to ream out the hole to a larger size, or even to bush it with a screwed copper bush. This obviously is a job for the boilersmith, who in any case should be called upon to examine the bridges between the tube holes for fractures and the holes themselves for ovality and possible reaming out circular and/or bushing, before retubing is commenced.

It has been found by long experience that less distortion of the tubeplate and outer rows of tube holes occurs when expanding starts at the outside rows by working inwards in a spiral manner to finish in the centre of the tube plate, than by any other alternative method.

When beading over the projecting end of the tube, it should be first roughly formed with the ball peen of the hammer and a conical drift and then, using the beading tool held at such an angle that the tube is forced against the plate. If held squarely to the tubeplate, the reverse effect will occur and the tube will give continual trouble from leaking.

The beading should be closed right down to the plate for two good reasons:
1. A gap will allow the sulphurous products of combustion to enter, which, combined with moisture, will start corrosion.
2. A gap will reduce the conductivity of the metal, consequently it will overheat and burn more readily.

Top left: A collapsed superheater flue caused by wastage. (*National Railway Museum*)

Bottom left: 'Necking' and perforation of a steel tube next to a copper tube plate arising from galvanic action. (*National Railway Museum*)

Below: A section of a collapsed flue tube at the element end of a superheater. (*National Railway Museum*)

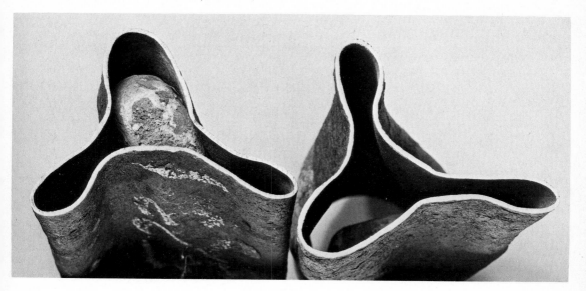

The ferocity of a boiler explosion is amply demonstrated in these four views of LNWR No 134 at Buxton in 1921, caused when the safety valves were out of adjustment and failed to release the excess pressure. *Above*: A general view of the boiler.

Below: The top of the firebox back plate.

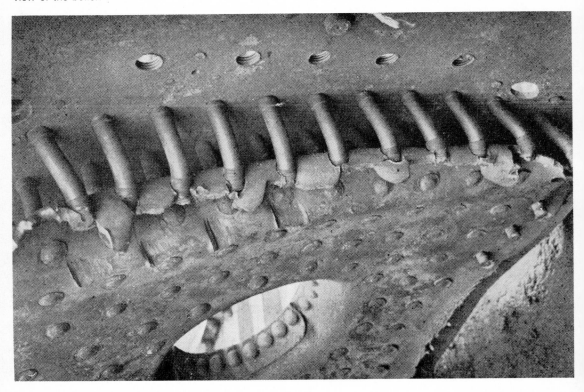

Above: the firebox wrapper plate.

Below: The firebox crown and girder bars. (*All H.M. Railway Inspectorate*)

Records and certificate of fitness

When odd tubes are removed or renewed for any reason, their position should be indicated – preferably on a scale drawing of the tubeplate (tubeplate diagram) with the date and by whom renewed.

It is important to make it clear to which end of the boiler the diagram refers, ie firebox or smokebox, as the top right tube in the firebox will appear as the top *left* hand tube on opening the smokebox door.

An alternative method of recording isolated tubes is to indicate their position thus:

Smokebox: 3rd tube down, 5th row from left.

The fitness of the boiler for service is the responsibility of the Boiler Inspector who will issue a certificate to this effect after satisfying himself that any repairs deemed necessary have been carried out satisfactorily.

The owner of the locomotive can, however, do much to prolong the life of its boiler by ensuring that it is kept thoroughly clean both internally and externally and not subjected to rapid or frequent changes of temperature.

WATER TREATMENT

A sample of the feed water normally used should be analysed by a water treatment specialist who will prescribe what treatment (if any) is necessary: his recommendations should be conscientiously applied. Samples of the treated water should be tested at regular intervals afterwards in order that any necessary corrections to the dosage can be made. World wide experience has proved the benefits of a chemically clean boiler.

COOLING DOWN

Rapid changes in temperature are extremely bad for a boiler and are the principal cause of tube and stay leakage, therefore, lower the temperature of a still hot boiler gradually by injecting cold water into it at the same rate as hot water is discharged at the blow-off cock.

This is done by connecting the cold water hose to the bayonet connection on the injector overflow pipe of BR standard engines or by pushing the hose up the overflow pipe where no connection is fitted and letting the cold water flow into the boiler via the clack valve. When the water flowing out of the blow-off cock is tepid, then and only

then is the boiler ready to be emptied and washed out with cold water.

For the same reason steam should be raised slowly in order that all parts of the boiler heat at a uniform rate.

BLOWING DOWN

If the boiler is fitted with a blow-down valve or cock that can be safely operated from ground level, such as the 'Everlasting' pattern, it is good practice on returning to shed to blow down two complete glassfulls, ie, commencing with the water level at the top of the gauge glass, to discharge sludge and sediment through the blow-down valve until the water level is in the bottom nut, then close the valve, refill the boiler with the injector and repeat.

With proper water treatment and regular blowing down an interval of 100 hours steaming between washouts should suffice for engines in daily use. Those used only occasionally should be washed out after every trip.

BOILER WASHING

Regular and thorough washing out of a locomotive boiler will do much to prolong its life, besides promoting free steaming and reducing coal consumption. Frequency of washing out will depend on the quality of the feed water in use; this can range from the soft peaty pure water of the mountainous districts of Scotland and Wales to the hard chalky water of Southern England where a good barrow load of hard scale is raked out of the boiler at every washout.

'Sifting' or the withdrawal of a proportion of the boiler tubes for the removal of sediment and scale was regular practice. BR's traction officer Bill Thorley recalls that on the Tilbury section of the LMS before the introduction of water softening, a third of the tubes of the 2-6-4 tanks were removed for this purpose every four months and an average of 27 cwt of dry scale was obtained at each 'sift'.

A hard coating of lime on the firebox plates and tubes is a poor conductor of heat and this causes the flanges or laps where there is a double thickness of plate to burn away. If the sludge that is precipitated when the water boils is not removed by frequent and thorough washing out it will accumulate in the narrow water spaces, above the foundation ring where the heat from the

Depressed firebox crown and tube plate arising from overheating as a result of lime encrustation. The localised depressions in the tube plate suggest the presence of girder bars. (*Author's collection*)

incandescent coal will bake it solid and burn the copper plate.

The normal appearance of the inside of a firebox in good condition is black, but should the soot be peeling off in flakes, exposing pink copper underneath – this is a sure sign of overheating. A boiler that has been short of water, will have this appearance down to the lowest water level, likewise 'mud burns' will be found just above the grate.

Requirements for washing out

1. An adequate supply of high pressure water (about 2,000 gallons of water is required to wash out a large boiler).
2. A pressure of 80 to 90 lb/square inch is required to project a jet of water from a $\frac{3}{4}$ inch diameter nozzle, with sufficient force to flush scale and sediment from a long boiler barrel which may be up to 20ft in length. One of the wartime Coventry Climax fire pumps is ideal for this purpose; failing which there are on the market centrifugal booster pumps.
3. A hose not less than $1\frac{1}{2}$ inch internal diameter that will reach easily from the pump or hydrant to the most remote part of the boiler is necessary.
4. At least two nozzles, one straight and the other bent at right angles at the tip, small enough to pass through a plug hole, so that a jet of water can be directed between the stays in the narrow water spaces are required. These should be copper or other soft metal in order to prevent damaging the screw threads in the plug holes.
5. Wash out rods of $\frac{1}{4}$ inch or $\frac{5}{16}$ inch diameter, one long slightly longer than the boiler barrel, and the other about 5ft long for rodding out the narrow water spaces. These rods have a ring at one end for handling, while an inch at

Left: Thorough washing out is vital for the avoidance of a build-up of lime and chalk deposits in hard water areas and generally to remove sludge. This is the mud hole door in the firebox of GW 0-4-2T No 1450 on the Dart Valley Railway. (*J. R. Besley, courtesy Dart Valley Railway*)

Right: Fig 2. Method of constructing a brick arch using an arch former.

the other extremity is bent at right angles and flattened to form a rake.

6. *Protective clothing* — Waterproof or oilskin leggings, jacket and footwear are 'a must' if the washing out process is to be done efficiently. Although a boiler *can* be washed out by one man with occasional help to turn on and off the water supply, it is done much quicker and better by two men, one to direct the jet and the other to turn 'on and off' and rake out. In order to do this efficiently he must assist the torrent of water gushing from a plug or hand hole by raking the dirt and scale towards him, hence the necessity for protective clothing.

Washing out procedure

1. Remove all washout plugs and inspection doors numbering them and their respective holes with chalk so that they go back in the same position. Be particularly careful to secure with stout string or wire those doors on top of the firebox, before knocking them in, or they may drop and become wedged in the water space and be extremely difficult or even impossible to retrieve.

2. Start with the firebox crown, paying special attention to raking out scale and sediment from between the roof stays and girder bars, if so fitted.

3. Next wash out the barrel, rodding out the firebox throat plate water space at the same time to prevent this becoming choked with scale.

4. Finally, wash out the firebox narrow water spaces giving particular attention to that part above the firehole ring, which is difficult to keep clean.

5. When all is clean, the boiler should be examined with a lighted paraffin torch (made from a piece of stout wire about four feet long with some asbestos string wound round one end and dipped in paraffin). This can be poked between the stays and gives a far better general illumination than does the beam from an electric torch for showing up any accummulations of scale that may have been missed. If the threads on the boiler stays can be seen and light is reflected from the wetted

surfaces and the plates and tubes 'ring' when struck with a hammer, this is a fair indication that the waterways, not all of which can be seen, are clear. On the other hand if the sound is dead or muffled, suspect an accumulation of scale.

6. *'Boxing up'*. Replace all washout plugs and inspection doors, first smearing the threads and joint faces with graphite grease; incrustation on threads should be removed with a wire brush.

Take great care to see that washout plugs are not put in cross threaded and tighten each as they are replaced. This is a far safer practice than first screwing in all plugs by hand and following up with a spanner later; a momentary distraction and one can be missed.

Should steam be seen coming from a plug when steam is raised, do not attempt to tighten it but allow the fire to die out and the pressure fall to zero when it can be dealt with safely. Plugs *have* been tightened under full steam pressure by men who well knew the possible fatal consequences of what they were undertaking and then only to avoid the

cancellation of a train, but it is *not* a practice to be recommended, certainly not by the inexperienced.

7. Finally a record of the washout and by whom it was done, should be entered on the engine history card, together with any special features that were noticed for future reference.

N.B. No reference has been made in these notes to washing out and re-filling with hot water in order to hasten return to traffic as was common on the railways in the days of steam. Such urgency is neither desirable nor necessary with preserved locomotives.

BRICK ARCH

Wide firebox engines and some narrow ones have arches constructed with two or three large interlocking bricks, variously known as 'Burrs', 'Quarls' or 'Quarries'. Narrow boxes generally have arches made of about thirteen small bricks like a house brick, only tapered. They are constructed on a scaffold, sometimes made of wood such as builders use when building an arch, or may take the form of an adjustable steel stand which is moved back as each row is completed.

BRICK ARCH

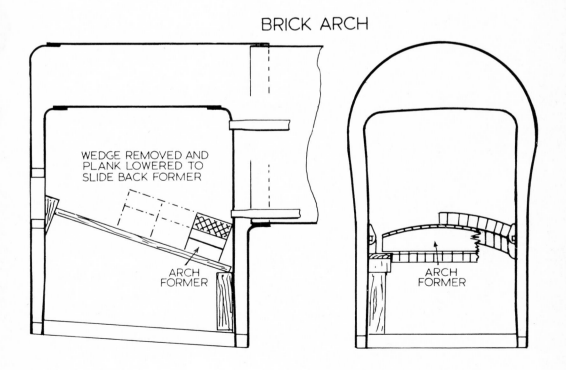

WEDGE REMOVED AND PLANK LOWERED TO SLIDE BACK FORMER

ARCH FORMER

ARCH FORMER

The large 'Burrs' or 'Quarls' need no scaffold, being lifted and held in position by the 'Bricky' and his mate.

The building of a secure brick arch in an old engine, having an almost parallel sided firebox, presents no difficulty but with a modern long narrow firebox with sloping curved sides it is quite another matter.

In this instance thin 1 inch bricks or 'slips' or perhaps pieces of slate, are inserted as necessary into the multibrick arch to ensure that it is of the correct camber and fits tightly between the side bricks.

It is disheartening to have it collapse in a heap of bricks, slippery with fireclay on removing the scaffold, but even this is better than having it collapse into the fire on the road.

Whichever type of arch is constructed, the mating surfaces should be liberally smeared with fireclay, and on completion the top strewn with broken glass. Old bottles or broken cab windows will serve. This glass will melt and fuse together in the interstices when fired, so strengthening and consolidating the whole.

Fit new carrier bars if these are at all burnt or twisted; *it is false economy not to do so.*

Uses for old firebricks

Old firebricks should not be discarded as rubbish. The larger pieces will serve to pave the bottom of smokeboxes and the remainder, broken to the size of a walnut, strewn on the grate before lighting up will prevent clinker adhering to the bars, thus making the task of fire cleaning much easier. Beach shingle is sometimes used for the same purpose.

STORAGE OF BOILERS

A boiler either wears out or rusts out and today the latter is the quicker of the two processes. The worst possible way to store a boiler is simply to empty it, leaving inside it all the wet sludge that starts active corrosion, especially around the foundation ring. The best way to store a boiler is to wash it out thoroughly and store in a dry atmosphere.

Swedish State Railways (SJ) has developed a very advanced technique of encapsulating a whole boiler in a gigantic plastic envelope to which is attached a de-humidifier. That this is undoubtedly the right method was convincingly demonstrated in India recently when the single

driver well tank locomotive *Fairy Queen*, built by Kitson's as long ago as 1855, was successfully steamed for the opening of the Indian National Railway Museum. Due to the hot, dry atmosphere no repairs whatsoever were required to the boiler which was last steamed in 1909.

French National Railways (SNCF) uses two methods of storing its boilers; after thoroughly washing out:

1. By filling them completely with water when there is no risk of frost damage.
2. Drying them out thoroughly by lighting a small fire in the middle of the grate and removing the dome cover to permit the damp air to escape. This is later replaced, together with all but one of the washout plugs; a small gas jet is inserted through the hole which, when all the oxygen in the air inside the boiler has been consumed, will go out. The last remaining plug is then replaced.

Tube plates, firebox interior and ashpan after being cleaned thoroughly are given a liberal application of waste oil with a brush.

The following modification of the second method is suggested as easily applicable at preservation centres.

1. Wash out.
2. Dry out with a small fire, taking care not to melt the plug.
3. Place small bags of silica gel in the water spaces in order to absorb moisture.
4. Box up.
5. Oil tube plates etc.

In order to combat corrosion by electrolytic action when a boiler that has a copper firebox is in steam, adopt Admiralty practice by placing zinc blocks in the boiler as an anode.

SAFETY VALVES

In the steam era the repair and adjustment of safety valves was considered so important that this work was confined to specialists in the main works, who, after the final adjustment, sealed the valve with a lead seal as well as stamping on the valve casting its authorised working pressure and registered number. A certificate to this effect was also issued and attached to the history card of the engine to which it was fitted.

No repair or adjustment of this vital boiler fitting should be made except under the supervision of the insurance company's inspector who will also be responsible for testing

Above: A 4in Ross pop safety valve.
Below: The Ramsbottom safety valve. (*Both National Railway Museum*)

Above: A fusible plug, clearly showing the softer plug centre. (*National Railway Museum*)

the boiler pressure gauge against a master gauge.

If anything more than grinding in or adjustment of spring tension by a shim of appropriate thickness is required, the valves should be removed from the boiler and sent to a railway works or specialist firm for attention.

FUSIBLE PLUGS

Fusible plugs have a central core filled with lead and are screwed into the firebox crown to give warning of a dangerously low water level; while covered with water the lead remains intact, but if uncovered only momentarily, the lead will melt and allow steam to escape into the firebox — so warning the crew.

This condition can be brought about by a false level of water showing in the gauge glass or an empty tank. Whatever the cause, there is a grave risk of the firebox crown becoming red hot and collapsing. Therefore the fire must be dropped or smothered with earth or ballast with the utmost urgency. In such an emergency, fire extinguishers from the train can be used with good effect.

Fusible plugs are commonly made to taper in three sizes of increasing diameter (A, B and C) to allow for wear and re-tapping of the hole in the firebox crown.

Particular care must be taken to see that the correct size of plug is fitted – also to avoid screwing it in cross-threaded.

The BR Standard fusible plug however has a parallel thread and relies for steam tightness on a faced joint with the firebox crown; the lead core is copper coated to prevent it being attacked by softened water.

The Boiler Inspector will decide on the frequency at which these plugs should be changed, depending on the days the boiler has been in steam. Refilling of lead plugs at the sheds was common practice at one time but has long since been forbidden, due to the difficulty in controlling the quality of workmanship and metal to a uniform standard.

WATER GAUGES

As the safety of the boiler depends on the maintenance of a proper depth of water above the firebox crown, it is essential that absolute reliance can be placed on the water gauges to show the true level.

Three cases of collapsed fireboxes with fatal consequences occurred during the war to American engines in Britain through the screw down type of water gauge fitting in use being partially closed and showing a false water level, whereas the position of a plug cock handle is immediately apparent.

This is possible also if the passages connecting the glass tube with the boiler become blocked or partially so. It was the practice at monthly intervals to prove these clear when the boiler was out of steam by removing the inspection cap nut and ball valves and with the plug cock open, passing a $\frac{1}{4}$ inch diameter rod or wire through the cock into the boiler water space. Even better is a square section rod measuring $\frac{1}{4}$ inch across corners as this will act as a reamer for removing hard scale.

When the engine is in steam, the bottom or drain cock should be opened at frequent intervals to drain the glass of water and on closing it the water should promptly rise to its former level and agree with the other gauge if they are duplicated.

When three independent cocks are fitted, ie, steam, water and drain, each passage can be proved clear as follows:

With the drain cock open, first close the middle or water cock, then steam should blow freely from the top or steam cock; secondly, close the

A water gauge showing the three independent cocks, the top for steam, the middle for water, and the bottom for draining. (*National Railway Museum*)

steam and re-open the water cock, when, if clear, the water will be heard roaring as it is discharged from the drain pipe. (Water roars, steam hisses.) Finally open both steam and water cocks and close the drain.

NB This procedure is not possible with coupled cocks.

Renewing gauge glasses

Remove the top cap nuts and unscrew the gland nuts, a brass flanged sleeve will then be seen. The purpose of this is to press the india rubber washer or ring into close contact with the glass, to make a steam-tight joint. More often than not this sleeve will have to be prised out of the fitting and the glass tube broken, owing to the rubber ring having perished and moulded itself into the gauge frame. The ring and remnant of the glass tube can be tapped out of the top fitting with a hammer and a piece of wooden dowelling – this is not possible with the lower fitting and the broken glass must be removed piece-meal, taking care not to cut any fingers in the process, as the jagged pieces are often reluctant to come out.

It is most important that every fragment of broken glass be removed and that the new glass goes right down to the bottom of the recess and *is kept there while the india rubber packing sleeve or cone is being tightened.* Failure to do this may result in the rubber sleeve slipping over the end of the tube and partially closing the bore, giving a false water reading.

'Klinger' packing sleeves. These have largely replaced the older asbestos fibre packed cock and are simple to change, the only precaution necessary being to see that the moulded rib on the sleeve slides into the groove in the fitting, also that the stainless steel eyelets do not drop out when the sleeve is tapped into position.

It is most important to see (and prove) that the handles are replaced on the correct square, especially with coupled cocks or a false water level will be shown.

Safety ball valves and restrictors. Care should be taken to see that these are replaced and in a clean condition after rodding the water ways; scale and corrosion may prevent these from seating properly in the event of a glass tube breaking.

The plate glass protector should never be removed while the engine is in steam without first closing the steam and water cocks. (Eyesight is far too precious).

In the event of a glass bursting and the ball valves not seating properly, smother the steam and scalding water escaping from the water cock with a sack, or even a jacket, so that the offending cocks can be shut off. The desirability of maintaining the water gauge cocks in an easily workable position will at once be apparent.

Water level indicator. A black and white diagonally striped enamelled iron plate is generally fitted behind the glass tube to show at a glance the water level. Due to refraction, the diagonal stripes when seen through water, appear to be horizontal but when seen through steam or air appear to slope more steeply.

In the absence of a striped back plate, newsprint held behind the glass will have the same effect, as the letters seen through water are reversed.

INJECTORS

Most live steam injectors today are of the under footplate or 'flooded' type, where the water from the tank flows to the injector by gravity. There is, however, another variety, the lifting injector which at one time was widely used, especially the combination or faceplate injector, in which the water is lifted to the injector cones by the vacuum created when it is set to work and this type may be encountered on some of the older engines.

The modern injector is an extremely reliable instrument and will continue to feed the boiler without waste at the overflow over a wide range of pressures ranging from blowing off point down to 25 lb/square inch or so. It will often be found difficult to start however much below 70 lb and few exhaust injectors will pick up cleanly below 90 lb/square inch, although as stated above, once working they will continue to deliver until the pressure is too low to lift the boiler clack.

Cold feed water, complete condensation and a perfect vacuum are essential requirements for any injector, and these conditions will not be attained if either the boiler clack valve or steam valve is leaking, allowing steam and hot water to heat the water in the feed pipe; this will not only not condense the steam, but will cause the water to boil as soon as a vacuum is created.

Similarly, air drawn in at leaking joints in the feed system will destroy the jet and prevent a vacuum being created, a vital point in the faceplate or lifting injector.

The cure for clack or steam valves blowing through is to grind in the former and to face up the latter in a lathe; if the seatings are scored or cut, then a special seating cutter is required. These were commonplace in the days of steam but are difficult to come by today and may have to be specially made.

Air leaks in the feed pipes can be readily found by plugging the overflow and blowing steam back into the tank; this is also a means of clearing temporarily a blocked tank sieve.

When an injector will not pick up cleanly, examine the cones, for they may be heavily coated

Above: A cut-away of a live steam injector; the steam feed is through the pipe on the right hand side, water feed through the orifice centre right, and delivery to the boiler from the left hand end through the clack and delivery pipe top left. (*National Railway Museum*)

Below: Class H exhaust injector. (*National Railway Museum*)

with lime. This can be dissolved in a dilute solution of hydrochloric acid. (Goggles should be worn as the acid effervesces and there is a risk of being splashed by bursting gas bubbles).

Alternatively, the movable portion of the combining cone may be drawing air and requires facing up. The hinged flap type seldom gives trouble but care should be taken when screwing in the delivery cone to see that the flap is uppermost. (This is marked with a letter 'T' in the Metcalfe exhaust injector for this purpose).

If, on examining the cones they are found in order, then a choked internal delivery pipe should be suspected, particularly where chalky water is used. It is the last few inches that become furred up and after 50 years I still retain vivid recollections of working head downward in the dome of an engine at Neasden in order to saw off the last foot of the internal delivery pipe. When retrieved, the $1\frac{3}{4}$ inch diameter pipe was furred up to such an extent that the orifice at its extremity was just big enough for a pencil to enter. Nowadays this task is performed with a rapidly rotating electrically driven steel burr.

Exhaust Injector

Messrs Davies & Metcalfe give the following as possible causes of their Class H exhaust injector not working:

If the injector fails to prime (ie, pick up the water) upon opening steam valve and steam escapes from the overflow, the trouble may be located in the water valve or the water valve piston.

If the injector primes and then flies off instead of going to work, the combining nozzle may be choked or the combining nozzle flap is not seating properly. *Sticking of the injector clack valve* or the *main boiler check* may also be responsible for trouble of this nature.

If the injector works with live steam but will not work with exhaust steam, either the automatic shuttle valve does not function or the exhaust valve *does not open.*

If the injector works with exhaust steam but will not work with live steam the shuttle valve may not function, or the exhaust valve may be *stuck open.*

If steam escapes in puffs from the overflow when injector is shut off with engine working steam, the exhaust valve is either stuck open or does not seat properly.

If water escapes at the overflow when injector is *not working* the water valve does not seat properly or may need grinding in.

If water and steam escape from the overflow when the injector is *not working* the boiler steam valve does not seat properly or may need grinding in.

If water escapes at overflow when injector is *working* and cannot be corrected by adjustment of the water regulator, the overflow valve may need grinding in or some of the injector cones may have become loose in the body. Alternatively, the ram that operates the overflow valve through a lever may be stuck fast in its gland.

To test the automatic changeover from live steam to exhaust steam and vice versa, apply engine brake with engine standing, start injector working and then open the regulator. If the automatic shuttle valve functions properly, the injector will stop working and water will run out of the overflow.

Then close the regulator and open the cylinder cocks. When pressure has escaped from the engine cylinders, the injector will immediately go to work.

If the injector does not operate as outlined above and continues to work with the regulator open, the automatic shuttle valve does not function.

Either a restriction will be found in the steam pipe leading from the main steam pipe of the locomotive to the injector, or the automatic check valve does not seat properly.

Cleanliness of water supply

No injector, especially the more complicated exhaust injector, can be expected to work properly if the feed is restricted by a partially blocked sieve or a dirty tank. This should be emptied and cleaned out at the end of every running season. It is surprising how much flaking scale, small coal and weed, etc, will accumulate inside.

Keeping the tank lid closed will ensure that coal does not fall in during coaling. Tank lids left open while passing under mechanical coaling plants, and water pick up scoops, ploughing through heaps of smoke box char carelessly thrown into the 'four foot' by lazy firemen and subsequently flushed into the tank when water was next picked up at the troughs, was the cause of much injector trouble and unnecessary work in the last days of steam on British Railways. This is now a thing of the past, but is cited as an example of what can occur if care is not taken to keep the tank clean.

Engine

POOR STEAMING

That 'Engineman Extraordinary' Bill Hoole, when asked what his favourite engines were, replied, 'Those that steam freely!' No matter how perfect an engine may be in other respects, if it does not steam freely it will not be popular with its crew, whereas one that will produce an abundance of steam will be forgiven its other faults. Rough riding engines frequently steam well, possibly due to vibration shaking ash and cinders through the grate. For one reason or another some designs of engine were always dull steamers, causing their crews much unnecessary care and anxiety in keeping time.

For these the 'jimmy' for sharpening the blast, or the 'false door' for restricting the ingress of cold air into the firebox when firing, and various other unorthodox devices, although frowned on officially, were the recognised tricks of the trade among enginemen.

Sometimes a hitherto free steaming engine will go off the boil and provided that neither coal nor fireman are at fault, the cause may be any one or combination of the following:

1. Dirty or clinkered fire.
2. Tube plate encrusted with fused slag blocking tubes.
3. Dirty tubes.
4. Choked ashpan restricting air supply to fire.
5. Air leaks in smokebox destroying draught.
6. Steam blows in smokebox destroying draught.
7. Blast striking one side of chimney – sometimes the result of a heavy and irregular deposit of carbon in the blast pipe.
8. Steam being wastefully used due to broken or badly worn piston/valve rings.

Non-steaming cases can be extremely baffling at times. First one defect is found and put right, but there is no improvement, then another with the same lack of result, until finally the 'full treatment' has to be given, ie, a water test and chimney alignment check.

Water test

This consists of filling the boiler, superheater header and elements and the steam pipes in the smokebox with water (preferably under mains pressure), when the slightest leak will become apparent.

Water under pressure is introduced into the boiler through the bayonet connection on the live steam injector overflow pipe on BR Standard engines or, through a connection screwed into a washout plug hole on others. The boiler is then completely filled, the regulator first being opened to allow air to escape and water to flow into the header, elements and steam pipes. When it is seen rising in the blast pipe, the pipe should then be plugged and the plug held in place with a screw jack and a beam of wood placed across the chimney cowl. The cylinder cocks must of course be closed, also the steam manifold isolating valve on the firebox, in order to permit water pressure to build up *and to prevent it flowing into places where it is least wanted such as vacuum brake cylinders*. Having to take down and drain four or five heavy vacuum brake cylinders that have become water-logged is a task that nobody wittingly repeats.

It sometimes happens that the pressure in the water main is insufficient to close the snifting valve. Closing the regulator to allow pressure to accumulate in the boiler and then reopening it smartly will sometimes seat the valve but, if it does not, then it must be blanked off.

It will be appreciated that once the steam supply valve to the auxiliaries at the manifold is closed, it is not possible to fill the vacuum brake exhaust, Westinghouse exhaust, or blower pipes with water. Generally a leak at a flange joint or union of these fittings will be betrayed by a white deposit on the otherwise sooty pipe. Quite a small flange joint blowing on the tube plate, (such as an anti-carboniser steam pipe) can have an effect out of all proportion to its size by destroying the draught through the tubes.

While the circuit is under water pressure, look carefully into the superheater flues, both at the smokebox and firebox ends, to see that there are no burst or perforated superheater elements. Water running out of a flue or tube will indicate that either it or the element it contains is perforated somewhere in its length. As soon as the defective joint or joints are located they must immediately be made good and the method will be found under the heading 'Joint Making'.

The test over, the level of water in the boiler is lowered to its normal level by opening the blow down valve and the cylinder drain cocks opened to drain the cylinders and steam pipes of water. The elements of superheater engines cannot be drained and care must be taken when moving the engine initially to do so slowly until all the water has been expelled from the cylinders, otherwise a broken piston or cover may result.

An alternative and neater method of water testing superheater engines that avoids filling the boiler is to remove the snifting valve and to connect the filling hose directly to the superheater header. In this way only the header, elements, steam pipes and cylinder are under hydraulic pressure as the regulator remains closed.

TESTING VALVES AND PISTONS

The life of piston rings and valve rings depends on the regularity and adequacy of their lubrication. Some classes of engines especially those using saturated steam, would run from shop to shop without requiring ring renewal. Others, particularly certain BR Standard, and some LMS classes, would not run more than ten to twelve thousand miles and frequently much less.

Worn or broken rings will generally be accompanied by a sharp increase in coal and water consumption and on starting away with a train, a hollow roar is heard coming from the firehole. When steam is escaping past worn rings a column of steam will issue from the chimney while the engine is stationary. Sometimes, however, the first indication of a broken valve ring is the presence of 'marbles' in the cylinder cocks.

A view from the underside of SECR 4-4-0 No 737, part of the National collection, showing the valve spindles and crossheads. (*National Railway Museum*)

Method of testing two-cylinder engines

Set the engine with both crossheads level with one another, ie, with one crank on the top front angle, the other on the bottom front angle. Apply the brake, open the cylinder cocks and place the reversing lever in mid-gear. In this position all steam ports should be closed and on opening the regulator no steam should issue from any of the four drain cocks. If it does, then the valve head adjacent to the cylinder cock from which steam is coming is defective.

Prove the valves steam tight and then, without altering the position of the engine, place the reversing lever in *forward gear*. This will open the RF port to steam and on opening the regulator, steam should come only from the front cock and not at all from the back. The left side is similarly tested by placing the reversing gear in *backward gear* which will open the LF port to steam.

A variation of this procedure when testing pistons is to *close* the cylinder cocks to ensure maximum build up of pressure in the cylinder and to listen and look for the roar of steam escaping from the chinmey top. This is a sure indication of live steam blowing past the rings to exhaust.

Method of testing three-cylinder engines

It is not possible to test all three valves and pistons at one setting as it is for the two-cylinder engine and therefore the 'mid-stroke' method must be used. Each big end in turn is placed on either top or bottom quarter and its valve tested first by putting the reverser into mid-gear and then the piston, by putting the lever into either full forward or backward gear.

Method of testing four-cylinder engines

The 'mid-stroke' procedure is used also for four-cylinder engines that have adjacent cranks at 180°, keeping in mind the fact that two cylinders will be receiving steam when testing pistons – one at the front and the other at the back.

LUBRICATION

Next to internal cleanliness of the boiler, no other factor will do more to prolong the life of a steam locomotive than adequate and constant lubrication of its moving parts while they are in motion. A hot box is a costly item to repair.

Extraction of water

Water, except in its proper place in the reservoir of a hydrostatic lubricator is the enemy of lubrication, for it will displace the oil in oil boxes, axlebox keeps and mechanical lubricators, destroying the syphoning action of the wicks or tails in the former and lifting the oil above the pump suction ports of the latter.

Ingress of water during washing out, condensation from blowing glands especially in the vicinity of the rear bogie wheels and sometimes heavy rain are common causes of axleboxes becoming waterlogged.

Axlepads

Draining of axlebox keeps (where drain plugs are provided) and extraction of water with a syringe after washing out should be a regular practice; if much water is present this should be squeezed out of trimmings and the tails of axlepads, by drawing through the fingers. If at all brown and gummy these trimmings should be renewed, also the axlepads if the tails have been reduced by chafing against the spring steel frame of the pad. Likewise, the axlepad should be renewed if its surface is glazed or the wooden buttons securing the fleece to the spring frame are exposed. Surprising as it may seem, it has been known for these to rub quite deep grooves in the journal. This is especially important where the axlepad is the sole means of lubrication as in a tender axlebox.

Care should be taken when renewing axlepads to see that they are of the correct length, ie, the full length of the journal; too short a pad will starve the collars of oil and, as the lateral thrust on these is very great, heating may well occur.

Waste packed axleboxes

These were all but universal on the Nigerian Railway and tests made there in 1938 proved that in order to saturate 10lb of cotton waste thoroughly, two days soaking in 12 gallons of warm axle oil was necessary. It was then allowed to drain for a further three days losing $8\frac{1}{2}$ gallons of oil in the process. The result was a springy, elastic material from which oil could be squeezed (although apparently dry) that did not drop away from the journal, unlike a soggy mass of undrained waste.

Only white cotton or wool waste should be used for packing and this should be twisted into three or four large rolls or 'sausages' and then packed into the keep with the ends turned underneath. This is done to prevent loose strands from being

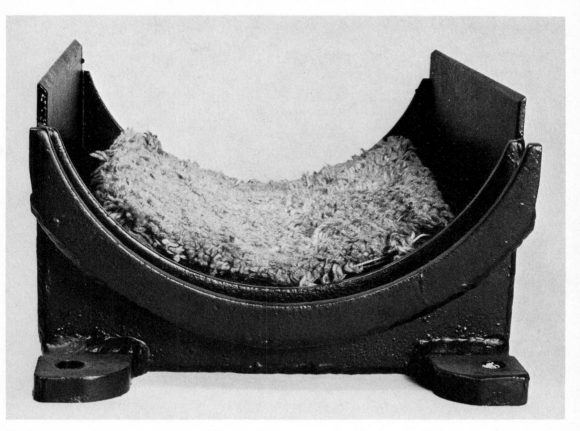

The keep and axle pad on an axlebox. It is essential that water should be regularly extracted to ensure adequate lubrication. (*National Railway Museum*)

drawn into the bearing and wiping off the oil. On no account should common coloured waste be used for packing as these are the sweepings from the mill floor and often contains pieces of wire and other foreign bodies.

A satisfactory alternative to waste packing is used on the Festiniog Railway by rolling up horsehair (recovered from old carriage upholstery) into balls about the size of an orange and binding them with worsted wool.

Worsted tail trimming

The quantity of oil delivered by a tail trimming is directly proportional to the number of strands in the 'tail' and increases until the point of restriction is reached; then the crowding of additional tails into the syphon tube will diminish the flow of oil until the trimming is in effect a plug trimming with a tail.

A trimming of two double strands, ie, four tails, will generally suffice for those parts having a small movement such as horn cheeks or valve spindle glands; double that number will be required for piston glands and slide bars but in the case of the latter the number of oil cups must be taken into account.

When making tail trimmings the wire frame should reach to the bottom of the oil cup or well, as it will cease to syphon when the level of oil in the oil box is at the same level as the lower end of the trimming.

The oil feed will be almost continuous when the oil box is brim full, but will quickly diminish to a rate of 2 to 3 drops a minute when the level of oil is half an inch or so below the top of the syphon tube and will almost cease at an inch below. For this reason, trimmings should not be put in, or alternatively oil boxes should not be topped up,

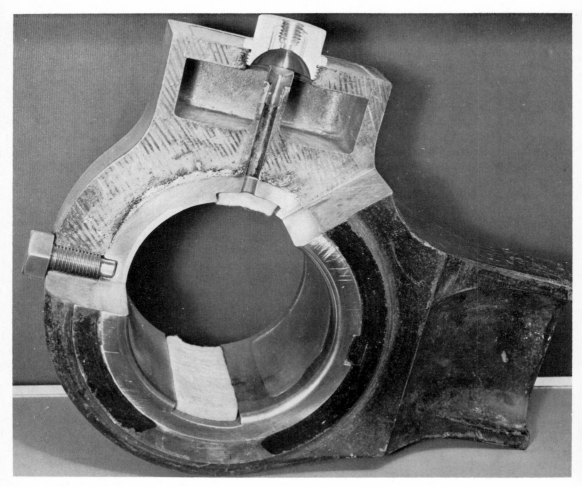

until shortly before the engine is due to leave the shed.

Failure to observe this rule results in oil running to waste, so making the engine unnecessarily oily and the inspection pits slippery, besides starving the engine of oil when it needs it most, ie, when it is working.

It is a good plan to trace and record the course of the more important oil pipes leading to the fast moving parts, so that in the event of say, a crosshead running dry, the trimming feeding its slidebar can be temporarily withdrawn and oil poured directly down the pipe.

Plug trimmings

No hard and fast rule can be laid down for the number of strands of worsted required for any particular application as this will depend on the bore of the syphon tube; $\frac{5}{16}$ inch and $\frac{3}{8}$ inch are common sizes. It should be tight enough to prevent it from being flung out by centrifugal force, yet not as tight as a cork in a bottle or no oil will pass to the bearing. A dry trimming that can be easily pushed down its syphon tube by pressure from the little finger, will be about the right fit when soaked with oil as it will swell slightly.

Pin trimmings

In the days when drivers each had their own engines and made their own trimmings, they regulated to a nicety the amount of oil that the big ends and coupling rods consumed on a given duty.

With the pooling of engines this know how ceased and the pin trimming and restrictor were devised to regulate precisely the supply of oil to the crank pins and big end journals.

Used by the former LNER and SR this consists of a small hexagonal cup screwed into the existing

LNER pattern solid big end with pin trimming. The big end has been cut away to show the oil tube. (*National Railway Museum*)

syphon tube to catch the oil as it is thrown around the oil reservoir, and has a needle or pin some four or five inches long working in a small hole in the centre of the cup. The clearance between pin and hole regulates the amount of oil passed to the bearing and is distributed by a felt pad let into the bush or brass. 13 swg pins are used in big ends and 12 swg pins in coupling rod oil wells. The up and down motion of the pin gives a pumping action to the oil; it also tends to wear the pin and enlarge the hole in the cup and gauges are provided so that worn pins and cups can be detected and changed as necessary.

The limits of wear for a standard cup and a 12 swg pin trimming using a numbered drill as a gauge are:

	New	Worn
Cup	31	30
No 12 Pin	36	37

Restrictors

Restrictors as used by the former GWR and LMS consist of a thick pad of felt let into the bush or brass. This not only distributes the oil but by its density regulates the flow of oil to the bearing. In addition there is a short plug with three flutes resembling a broken plug tap screwed into the syphon tube. The prime purpose of this restrictor is not so much to regulate the flow of oil (which is controlled by the density of the felt pad) but to prevent a worsted trimming mistakenly being inserted in the tube.

The disadvantage of this arrangement is that it is necessary to take down the rods in order to renew the felt pads when oil consumption becomes excessive. Pads should be cut slightly oversize to ensure a degree of compression when pressed into the slot in the bush.

The work involved in taking down motion and rods for this purpose is considerable and a compromise has been satisfactorily effected on LNER V2 2-6-2 No 4771 by restricting the restrictor to the middle big end so that it passes approximately the same amount of oil as a pin trimming.

This was achieved by bending back on themselves the legs of a $\frac{5}{32}$ inch diameter split pin, in such a way that their rounded sides filled almost completely two of the flutes in the restrictor when inserted therein. Subsequent experience showed that yet further restriction was necessary and this was done by inserting one leg of an $\frac{1}{8}$ inch split pin down the third flute.

This engine has now run over 2,500 miles hauling fast and heavy trains with an oil consumption consistent with the designed capacity of the oil well, ie, 400 miles. Formerly the oil well would be found more than half empty after running 50 miles and it was as much the difficulty in procuring felt of the right density as the difficulty in finding sufficient staff to undertake the removal and re-erection of the centre connecting rod, that prompted this solution of the problem.

It gives confidence to know how far a bearing will run on a given quantity of oil; this is easily established by using a dip stick once the capacity of the oil reservoir has been measured.

Corks

Oil wells are closed by a variety of methods, by a cork or cane screwed directly into the oil well cover, in the case of engines fitted with restrictors by a screwed bronze cap into which a cork is screwed, or a cap incorporating a spring loaded ball valve.

Porous corks or canes to allow air to enter as the oil is displaced and so prevent an air lock occurring is a peculiarly British institution; elsewhere on the Continent of Europe and in America they seem to manage well enough without.

Excessive force is not required in screwing home a cork or the thread cut in it will be stripped and/or the cork broken. Furthermore, in engines fitted with restrictors it is possible to screw down the cork to such an extent that it effectively plugs the restrictor itself. As a consequence, in both these cases, a hot bearing will result; either the cork will be thrown out together with the oil, or in the second instance the oil supply will be cut off.

It is false economy therefore not to renew corks when they become at all loose. When the supply of cane centred corks common in steam days is exhausted consideration should be given to using short pieces of cane of $\frac{1}{2}$ inch diameter and about three inches long, with two flats pared on the upper end to facilitate screwing in. This was the

Left: Adequate preparation of an engine for the road is essential. The author oils round former LNER 2-6-2 No 4771 *Green Arrow* at Leicester in 1973. (*Leicester Mercury*)

Right: The Wakefield No 7 mechanical lubricator. (*National Railway Museum*)

method used by the GER and many other companies. Cane has the advantage of being more durable, stronger and, unlike a cork, all the capillaries run axially allowing it to 'breathe' better.

Sight feed or hydrostatic lubricators

Like the mechanical lubricator, dirt is the enemy of the sight feed lubricator by blocking the fine bore holes in the nipples. Frequent blowing out with steam in accordance with the makers' instructions and, even more important, keeping oil bottles clean will ensure trouble free service.

If the sight glass has become cloudy by an accumulation of oil at the top due to too rapid a feed, it and the lubricator will benefit by putting a knob of washing soda in the oil reservoir when this has been emptied, turning on the steam and boiling out, after which it should be drained and refilled with clean oil. A rate of three to four drops per minute will give adequate lubrication to both valves and pistons.

In the case of the Detroit lubricator the atomiser non-return valves should be reversed when worn and renewed when both ends are worn.

Mechanical lubricators

These are of two main types, double acting and single acting, the 'Silvertown' lubricator used by the former LMS adopted as the BR standard is a good example of the former and the Wakefield No 7 used by the LNER of the latter.

The oil pumps are driven from some part of the motion having a constant movement such as the eccentric rods of Stephenson's valve gear or from the expansion link in the case of Walschaert's.

It is not good practice to drive the lubricator from the valve spindles as the movement diminishes as the engine is notched up. The NER overcame this difficulty by providing an ingenious arrangement of a cam slot in the link driving the 'Hulburd' valveless lubricator fitted to its engines.

The lubricator shaft revolves in one direction only, whereas the engine must go both backwards and forwards, so motion to the cam shaft oscillating the pump is imparted by a pawl engaging with a toothed wheel having 100 teeth in the case of the Wakefield No 7.

Whether single or double acting, most mechanical lubricators are designed to deliver 2oz of oil per 100 miles. In the case of the Wakefield No 7 the pawl should gather three teeth at each return stroke ie, a certain 'three' and an occasional 'four', according to the amount of backlash in the linkage. Most modern engines have only two pin holes provided in the linkage ie, one for ex Works, the other for normal running, whereas older engines had a multiplicity of pin holes in the linkage (which was generally of crude design), permitting literally hundreds of combinations and if ill adjusted, as was often the case, resulting in a very slow and erratic rotation of the oil pump cam shaft.

Each individual pump of the Wakefield No 7 lubricator is capable of adjustment; when screwed

A badly carbonised blast pipe, reduced to less than half its original diameter as a result of too much oil over a long period. (*E. Maugham, Gorton*)

right down (clockwise) full feed is given, *when unscrewed* five complete turns no motion at all is given to the pumps. LNER instructions were that both axlebox and cylinder lubricators should be set at $\frac{2}{5}$ feed.

A gummy interior of the blast pipe and a crust of carbon round its orifice is an indication that the oil feed requires reducing.

Some industrial locomotives have only one mechanical lubricator to serve both cylinders and axleboxes; in such a case a dual purpose oil such as Shell 'Valvata' is required.

When testing the delivery of oil to an axlebox from a mechanical lubricator it is not sufficient to see oil oozing from the test cock. Make sure that it is actually getting to the bearing by disconnecting or slackening the flexible hose at its point of delivery to the axlebox.

Metallic hoses sometimes break and the lining of india rubber hoses will perish and collapse with age, obstructing the flow of oil. This check may well avert a hot box.

It is good practice to remove the drain plug from the mechanical lubricator reservoir occasionally to see whether water is present; if it is, it is an indication that the atomiser/anti-carboniser, non-return valves are blowing through and letting steam blow back into the

lubricator where it condenses. The usual reason for this is dirt or grit preventing the ball valves from seating, due to a gradual accumulation of ash, coal, dust etc., in the lubricator caused by the use of dirty oil bottles and the piercing or removal of the fine gauze sieve from the lubricator in cold weather to allow the thick 'Black Jack' to flow more quickly into the lubricator, rather than waiting until it becomes fluid by warming it on the boiler front.

Foreign matter in a mechanical lubricator can cause mischief out of all proportion to the slight extra work involved in keeping oil vessels clean. First and foremost, if lubrication to the rapidly moving valves and pistons is interrupted for any length of time, undue wear and possibly scoring of cylinders and valve liners will occur. One has only to listen to a dead engine groaning as it is being dragged about, to visualise the consequences of an interruption to the oil supply at speed.

The importance of keeping everything connected with lubrication perfectly clean cannot be stressed too strongly. Oil bottles in particular should be cleaned out frequently, either by boiling out with caustic soda or hosing out with hot water from the coal slaking hose and when clean, kept stoppered to exclude coal, ash, dirt and water.

Soft grease lubrication

In order to improve further its availability for service, the later steam locomotive incorporates in its design some features of automobile practice such as grease lubricated roller bearings that will run from shed day to shed day without intermediate attention. Typical applications are roller bearing axleboxes, valve motion, brake gear and heavily loaded parts like bogie and pony truck slides.

The 'Tecalmit' system of soft grease lubrication whereby grease is forced into a bearing either by a hand or pneumatically operated grease pump or gun terminating in a flexible hose with a clip-on head for attaching to the special nipple incorporating a non-return valve, is all but universal. A heavy duty grade of grease such as 'Alvania', which has a lithium base, is required and the roller bearing makers' lists of approved brands should be consulted.

As with oil lubrication, water is the enemy of grease lubricated roller bearings, especially such highly loaded applications as axleboxes, where fretting corrosion of the hardened surfaces of cups and rollers can, and does, lead to flaking and the ultimate break up of the bearing.

For this reason, some makers specify a 'sponge' grease that will absorb and emulsify moisture. The normal appearance of grease in a roller bearing axlebox is grey and if it has a whitish-yellow appearance it has emulsified and must be removed, the bearing thoroughly cleaned with petrol and then recharged with clean, uncontaminated grease.

Timken taper roller bearing axleboxes as used on BR Standard engines, are provided with an air vent and it is important that the makers' instruction not to overcharge the bearing is observed.

When greasing the valve motion or brake gear, etc, cease pumping as soon as a film of grease exudes from the bearing and wipe off the surplus grease. If left, not only will it attract dust and dirt, but more important still, it can then be seen immediately that it is new and not old grease that is coming from the bearing.

If grease exudes from the clip-on attachment to the grease nipple instead of the bearing, this may be due to the presence of dirt, and it is good practice to wipe the nipples clean before clipping on the grease hose. If cleaning does not effect a cure then the nipple is blocked and must be changed.

Independent grease cups

These are of the screw down type, where a certain amount of air is imprisoned in the cup. This expands at the normal running heat of the bearing, so displacing an equivalent quantity of grease. The LNER used a cup of this type (the 'Menno' grease cup), on the two-to-one valve gear pins of its three-cylinder engines as first built; it was subsequently replaced by pressure gun nipples first of the 'Enots' and then later of the 'Tecalmit' system.

Many plain bearing motion pins are also lubricated with soft grease and an interval of 500 to 600 miles between greasing would be appropriate for such applications. However, as preserved locomotives work only occasionally and sometimes the interval between trips is long, it is suggested that greasing be done as a matter of routine when the engine is prepared, acting on the principle that it is better to over-grease than under-grease an engine.

VACUUM BRAKE

Locomotives operating passenger trains over BR metals must comply with BR regulations respecting the efficiency of the continuous automatic brake system.

Tests to be applied

1. *Obstruction test.* Remove the rear hose connection from its dummy and fully open the large ejector; if more than three inches of vacuum can be obtained then an obstruction exists somewhere in the train pipe between the rear hose and the vacuum ejector and this must be searched for and removed. Repeat for the front hose connection if fitted, after replacing the rear one on its dummy.

A common cause of obstruction is a sponge cloth sucked out of a shunter's hands when coupling up; likewise strands of cotton waste drawn into the reducing valve or governor can get under the several air clacks and cause an internal leakage. A cloth or ball of waste drawn in at the hose coupling will generally be found at the first elbow that it encounters in its passage towards the ejector, frequently at the elbow at the base of the hose swan neck stand pipe.

For these reasons **it is forbidden** for waste or cloths to be placed in the vicinity of the ejector reducing valve or near the hose connection when coupling up train pipes.

The vacuum hose couplings should be provided with cross wires to prevent articles like sponge cloths being drawn into the system.

On occasions an obstruction can be very difficult to locate and may involve pulling much piping apart before it is eventually located.

2. *Ejector efficiency test.* The working vacuum is 21 inches and the reducing valve or governor must be adjusted so that this amount is created but not exceeded when both large and small ejectors are fully open.

Having set the reducing valve, the capacity or efficiency of the large and small ejectors are tested in turn by introducing an artificial leak into the system to simulate the normal leakage on a long train, due to the aggregate of a number of minute leaks none of which, individually, would be sufficient to fail a vehicle.

3. *Small ejector*. This should be capable of maintaining 21 inches of vacuum against a $\frac{3}{16}$ inch diameter hole in the leak disc.

4. *Large ejector*. Should maintain 21 inches of vacuum against a $\frac{1}{4}$ inch diameter hole. Should either large or small ejector fail to achieve the prescribed standard, the cones should be examined for wear or scale deposit in the case of an annular jet ejector, such as the 'Dreadnought'. When removing scale, care should be taken not to damage or wear away the relatively soft bronze cone.

5. *Leak discs*. Can be easily made from a circular piece of thin plate to which an india rubber hose washer is cemented, one having a $\frac{3}{16}$ inch and the other a $\frac{1}{4}$ inch diameter hole drilled through its centre. Frequently holes of both sizes are combined in one disc, with a small movable vane or flap to cover either one or the other hole. Sometimes a vacuum hose pipe connection complete with connecting horn and lugs is plugged and drilled for the same purpose; this often has a test gauge attached and it has the advantage that it will not drop off the hose when the vacuum is destroyed.

6. *Leakage tests*. Having established that both ejectors are efficient, the apparatus on engine and tender is next tested for external and internal leakage in the following manner.

7. *External leakage*. With the brake application handle in the running position create 21 inches of vacuum with the small ejector and then close the small ejector steam valve and time the rate of fall of the train pipe vacuum to 12 inches.

On engines with vacuum brake cylinders this time should not be less than 30 seconds, on engines fitted with a through pipe only, 20 seconds is the minimum allowed.

Should this standard not be attained, re-open the small ejector and search for the leak (which can often be heard) with a lighted flare lamp or candle, holding it against each pipe joint in turn commencing at the front hose washer; the flame will be drawn in at the point where air is entering;

Hose washers not seating perfectly or dirty drip valves and leaking vacuum cylinder neck ring bushes are common faults; leaking pipe unions can be tightened but not screwed pipe couplings, short of taking down. Minor leaks at couplings and elbows may be sealed with rubber solution.

Vacuum operated steam brake valves. To enable steam braked engines to work vacuum fitted stock, they are equipped with an ejector for creating a vacuum in the train and a combination valve which on a reduction in vacuum, automatically allows steam to enter the engine brake cylinder.

On older engines this steam valve is held on its seat by atmospheric pressure acting on a vacuum piston, communicating internally with the vacuum train pipe. A worn piston will allow air to enter the train pipe, re-metalling and turning to a neat fit in its cylinder is the remedy in this case.

Modern engines with Mark VI Graduable steam brake valves are provided with diaphragm of neoprene instead of a piston, which are much more reliable but do crack after prolonged use, especially when exposed to heat.

8. *Internal leakage*. This applies only to engines fitted with vacuum brake cylinders; create a vacuum of 21 inches and then destroy the *train pipe vacuum* by applying the brake.

There will be a momentary drop in the *chamber side vacuum* due to the displacement of the pistons in the brake cylinders. As soon as a vacuum of 21 inches has been re-established close the ejector and note what fall, if any, there is in the chamber side vacuum. Several minutes should elapse before there is any appreciable drop in vacuum, but should the chamber side needle fall almost immediately, this is a fair indication that a rolling ring or sliding band is defective.

If more than one vacuum brake cylinder is fitted these should be isolated in turn by blanking off the ball valves, or if of the internal type, at the Tee piece thus avoiding unnecessary labour in taking down and stripping any but the defective cylinder.

Vacuum brake cylinders

Cylinders of large diameter are particularly heavy and cumbersome to handle in the confined space beneath a locomotive. A most useful piece of equipment for lifting or lowering these heavy articles safely and easily is a steel tripod with a long central screw, not unlike a tall music stool.

The Dreadnought vacuum ejector and driver's brake
handle. (*National Railway Museum*)

Rolling rings

These must be free from twists or they will not roll properly. The moulded fin on the roller ring will indicate whether or not it is twisted; plucking it from its groove at several points round its circumference will release the twist.

Bent piston rods

If persistent trouble is experienced with a roller ring twisting, the piston rod is probably bent in the neck, thus canting the piston. This should be checked between lathe centres.

Neck rings drawing air

This may be due to a badly worn piston neck ring bush, caused by partial seizure of the cylinder trunnion bushes, thus preventing it from rocking freely.

Leakage on the train

If the train is operating over BR lines with BR stock it is BR's responsibility to locate and rectify any fault developing in the brake system, but a knowledge of the procedure adopted will be useful to operators on private railways.

The following procedure was developed during the second world war to reduce to a minimum the time taken to locate a vacuum leakage on the exceptionally long trains then prevailing and is now contained in the Appendix to the Rule Book:

1. With 21 inches showing on the engine gauge, a minimum of 18 inches must show at the rear van of a passenger train and not less than 16 inches for a fitted freight train.
2. If this cannot be achieved, disconnect the engine and test it as set out under Tests to be Applied, No 1 to 7, checking also the accuracy of the engine gauge with a master gauge.
3. The engine having been proved satisfactory, re-connect to the train and proceed to divide and sub-divide the train as follows:

   Assuming that we have a train of 24 vehicles, divide the train between the 12th and 13th vehicle and test the front half, if this is satisfactory then the fault must be in the rear half. Reconnect this to the front half and again divide between the 18th and 19th vehicles and if still satisfactory then the fault must be in the last six vehicles. Continue to sub-divide until the defective coach is found.

   Do *not* be tempted to run up and down the train listening for leaks unless it is very short indeed as it wastes valuable time and is often futile. The longer the train, the quicker a leak is found by adopting the methodical procedure outlined above.

Brake adjustment

It is very important with power brakes such as the vacuum, steam, or compressed air to ensure that the blocks are firmly applied to the wheels well before the brake piston has reached the extremity of its stroke.

The vacuum brake when combined with compensating brake gear is especially liable to loss of brake power through the piston going right up before all the slack has been taken out of the rigging; at least three inches of piston stroke should remain in reserve.

Adjustment is usually effected by a turnbuckle or quill having a right and left hand thread; when the limit of adjustment of this quill is reached, it must be unscrewed and the slack taken up by moving the pin in the brake shaft arms to another hole in the pull rod.

Before making an adjustment see that the brake piston (or pistons) are 'off', that is right down in the case of the vacuum brake, and right 'up' or 'in' in the case of a steam or Westinghouse brake.

Both steam and air brakes require a certain movement of the brake piston to give the most effective brake and it will be found that a clearance of approximately $\frac{1}{2}$ inch between the bottom of the brake block and the tyre will provide the necessary travel.

On the other hand the vacuum brake with its increased leverage, due to its lower power, requires taking up closely to the wheel. If the blocks can be shaken when the brake is released then there is sufficient clearance, but the blocks must not be so tight as to cause them to bind should a driving wheel drop into a low place in the road, a not uncommon experience in shed yards where drainage is poor. Late starts have been caused through having to slack out the brake on the level if another engine has not been available to assist.

Adjustment is best made when the engine is in steam; one or two applications of the brake will soon show whether or not the adjustment made has been sufficient. This is especially so in the case of LNER engines where the turnbuckle cannot be rotated unless the brake pull rods are disconnected from the brake shaft; this particular arrangement was adopted as the result of a near

An underneath view of the vacuum brake cylinder (above the nearest axle) on SECR 4-4-0 No 737, together with the vacuum reservoirs mounted above the bracket further forward, and the brake rigging. (*National Railway Museum*)

accident to a petrol train which ran away due to the brake on the engine slacking out, which is possible with the usual left and right hand threaded turnbuckle.

To make an effective brake adjustment on such engines a screw shackle or, better still, a Yale 'Pullift' is necessary to take up the slack in the rigging. In the absence of either of these facilities, improvise a 'Spanish Windlass' or tourniquet, using a wagon rope.

WESTINGHOUSE AIR BRAKE

The Westinghouse air brake is more powerful and releases more quickly than does the vacuum brake and was for this reason retained right up until the end of steam on the celebrated 'Jazz' services out of Liverpool Street to Chingford and Enfield with their electric traction timings.

'Four fifths of the world's railways are air braked'; this used to be the Westinghouse company's advertising slogan; when used correctly and properly maintained, it is a sure and powerful brake. The French *mécaniciens de la route* were experts with the Westinghouse. A single application only was made to give the desired amount of pressure in the brake cylinder. The handle of the driver's valve was put into *bloc* or the lap position and kept there until the train had all but stopped, then it would be released and the train brought smoothly to a halt.

If, however, it is mishandled or badly maintained it can be treacherous and leave the driver with little or no brake power. The man unskilled in its use will make repeated applications and releases, forgetting that every time he does so he is lowering the pressure in the auxiliary reservoirs and that these cannot be recharged until the brake handle has been put into full release for perhaps a minute or more, not wise when descending a steep gradient with a heavy train.

It is for this reason that our modern air braked trains have two pipes, one to keep the auxiliary reservoirs fully charged and the other to operate the triple valves, or distributors as they are called today.

Earlier, simpler types are still to be found on several of our preserved locomotives however. For example the GER Y14 at Sheringham, like most of that company's older engines, has no governor for its small $6\frac{1}{2}$ inch pump, which retains the original pattern of vertical shuttle valve. The driver's and triple valves too, are of the original simple pattern. The LB&SC version of the Westinghouse brake as fitted to the Stroudley Terriers could be aptly described as the 'Brighton air brake'.

At the other end of the scale is the sophisticated apparatus to be found on preserved Continental engines such as compound air compressors, self lapping driver's valves and the German variant, the Kunz Knorr.

Draining of reservoirs

A common cause of loss of brake pressure is failure to drain the reservoirs of the condensate that accumulates in them, thereby reducing the volume available for compressed air to a dangerous level.

Air pump stopping

Should the pump stop either through lack of lubrication or a mechanical fault the effect will be the same. Faced with such an emergency, enginemen often resorted to hammering the steam cylinder of the pump with the coal pick (as many old photographs disclose) in the hope that this would jar it into activity!

If a light tap does not start the pump ($8\frac{1}{2}$ inch type), try slackening the three nuts holding on the cover of the differential piston valve; this will release the pressure and should cause the valve to reverse and so start the pump working. If this fails then it may be that the rings on the differential piston valve are worn or broken. This valve can be extracted by screwing a $\frac{1}{4}$ inch Whitworth bolt into a tapped hole provided for this purpose in the larger of the two pistons.

The rings of these pistons are very fragile and break easily, especially when worn thin. Great care is, therefore, necessary in replacing the valve.

A useful tip to prevent badly worn rings from dropping below the ring groove is to fill the groove with thick grease, but if they are so badly worn as to require this expedient they need renewing.

Reversing plate

Another cause of a pump stopping is a deeply indented striking or reversing plate attached to the steam piston. At every stroke made by the piston the reversing plate either pushes up or draws down a slender spindle to which is attached a horse shoe shaped reversing valve.

Indentation of the reversing plate (which has a keyhole shaped slot in it to engage with the spindle) will upset the valve events and must therefore be renewed.

The reversing plate can be reached by removing the steam cylinder top head together with its reversing valve and spindle, taking care not to bend it when disengaging it from the reversing plate.

Two pairs of hands are better than one for this operation or the delicate spindle may be bent. Rolling its larger diameter on a flat surface will quickly reveal if it is bent, in which case it must be carefully straightened.

Reversing rod

Occasionally the reversing rod is found to be broken, usually through metal fatigue. A competent mechanic should find no difficulty in repairing or renewing a broken spindle or making a new reversing plate from mild steel.

Lubricator

Lack of lubrication through the tiny hole or choke in the displacement lubricator becoming blocked with dirt is probably the most common cause of a pump stopping and the remedy for this is scrupulous cleanliness. Conversely the choke may have become so enlarged that the oil is soon exhausted. One charge should suffice for seven to eight hours work.

Worn piston rings

The small $6\frac{1}{2}$ inch pump should, with steam pressure of 125 lb/square inch charge the main reservoir to a pressure of 90 lb/square inch in $4\frac{1}{2}$ minutes and the $8\frac{1}{2}$ inch pump in three minutes. If it does not and there is no reduction in the rate of pumping as main reservoir pressure increases,

Above: The Westinghouse compressed air brake survived in use on a few steam locomotives in Britain until the end of regular BR steam operation, while others retained the equipment even though it was not regularly used for train working. This is an 0-4-4T on the Isle of Wight, where the Westinghouse brake survived exclusively until electrification. This view shows the compressor mounted on the left side of the smokebox and the air reservoir on top of the tank. Other types of compressed air brake are used on certain European locomotives preserved in Britain.

Right: 'Why won't it work?' The Westinghouse pump on preserved LTSR 4-4-2T *Thundersley*. (*Arnold Hoskins*)

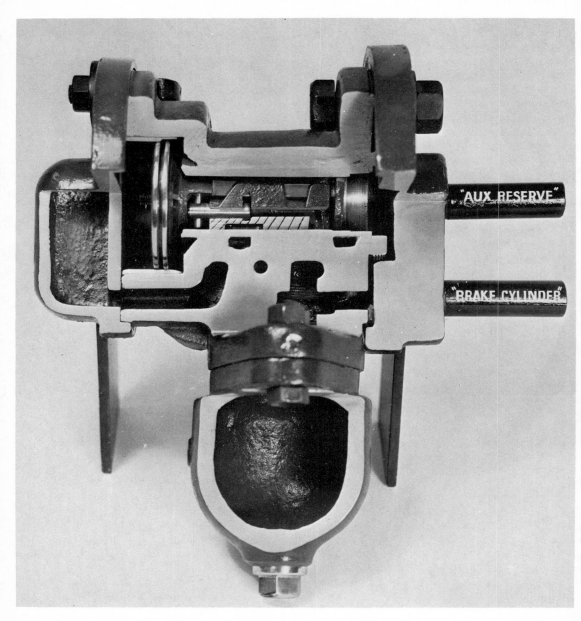

this is an indication that air is either escaping through the air clacks or past the piston rings. However, before arriving at this conclusion make sure that air is not escaping from the system elsewhere, first by isolating engine and tender triple valves and then opening these in turn until the source of leakage is located.

The remedy for worn piston or valve rings in the steam driven air compressor is the same as that outlined for the engine pistons.

Triple valve

These give little trouble provided they are kept scrupulously clean and lubricated every 21 to 30 days with 'Paragon' grease or a light mineral oil.

Driver's valve (Original Pattern)

This differs from the modern valve in combining in a single spring loaded valve the dual functions of an excess pressure and discharge valve. This is achieved by reducing the pressure

The Westinghouse improved triple valve for automatic compressed air brakes. The connection to the train pipe is through the port, bottom left. (*National Railway Museum*)

on the excess pressure/discharge valve spring through the medium of a quick start screw thread to which the application handle is attached. An angular movement of approximately 120° from full release to an emergency application suffices to reduce the pressure on the spring from 90 lb/square inch to zero.

This old pattern driver's valve also contains a small spring loaded feed valve which maintains a constant pressure differential of 15 to 20 lb/square inch between the brake pipe (70 lb/square inch) and the main reservoir when in the running position.

The strength of these springs is critical, especially the short stiff discharge valve spring, the length of which when fully compressed is only slightly less than when completely unloaded. When these springs get tired through loss of temper full reservoir pressure cannot be achieved.

If an attempt is made to increase spring tension by the addition of a thin washer, this has the disconcerting effect of restricting the free discharge of air in an emergency application and **is, therefore, dangerous.** Replacement by a new spring with the correct characteristics and properly tempered is the answer to this problem.

Brake cylinders

The cup 'leathers' of these are nowadays made of neoprene, but if still of leather it must be kept supple by the introduction of neats foot or lard oil at the 21 to 30 day examination. If allowed to get dry and harden, air will blow past the piston without expanding the cup leather.

Brake adjustment

In order that the piston may pass the leakage groove in the cylinder a minimum travel of two inches is required but the maximum travel should not exceed four inches.

Westinghouse/Vacuum combination valve (simple type)

Adjust the spring pressure until the air valve is on the point of opening when the train pipe vacuum is reduced to 12 inches of mercury. When working in combination with this type of valve,

the driver's brake valve handle must be placed in the block or lap position, otherwise the feed valve will admit air at the same rate as it is being released by the combination valve.

Position of cock handles

These differ from normal practice in that when the handle is across the pipe the cock is open and when in line with it, it is closed; bent handle cocks however, are an exception and follow normal practice.

RUNNING REPAIRS

The scope of repairs that can be undertaken will depend on the facilities (or lack of them) at the preservation centre concerned. Some are fortunate in having inherited a large concentration depot complete with wheel drops, electric hoists, wheel lathes and a variety of essential machine tools, while other make do in an old goods shed without a pit or perhaps even in the open.

Protection from the weather is probably as important as a pit in expediting repairs but even these evidently are not essential and one can only marvel at the courage and enterprise of those who roll out driving wheels from under an engine, in the open and on the level, solely by means of jacks and sleeper packing and much hard graft.

Machine tools are necessary only when such major overhauls as reboring and refacing axleboxes, renewing coupling and connecting rod bushes, re-turning piston rods, re-metalling and planing crossheads, etc, are undertaken.

Once an engine has been put into good working order, it should, with proper care and attention, run for 30 to 40,000 miles without needing other than hand tools for its maintenance.

In steam days it was exceptional to find as much as a drilling machine at small sheds with an allocation of anything from six to 24 engines. The Cheshire Lines was remarkable in having no machine tools at all, even at a large shed like Trafford Park. A good selection of hand tools and a competent staff sufficed to keep its stud of locomotives in good working order. The old adages of 'a stitch in time' and 'prevention being better than a cure' are especially applicable to locomotive maintenance.

Minor defects and adjustments

In days gone by it was common practice at small sheds where there was no artisan staff for the drivers and firemen themselves to do the necessary maintenance at the 'shed day', such as washing out the boiler, sweeping tubes, renewing firebars, packing glands, etc, under the supervision of the Driver in Charge who received a small extra payment for this added responsibility.

It was only when some defect developed beyond their capacity or when a periodical examination became due that an out-station engine was exchanged for another from the district shed.

Hand tools

A range of spanners, both open jaw and ring to fit every nut and union on the engine, including 'C' spanners for rack nuts, plus a brake spanner and washout plug key are obviously essential, together with a selection of box spanners to extract injector cones etc.

A $1\frac{3}{4}$ lb hand hammer and 7 lb hammer and a variety of chisels, bars and pin punches are likewise essential.

A stout bench with a strong, secure six inch vice and a selection of flat, round and square files will enable most running repairs to be undertaken.

Care of tools

Buy the best tools that you can afford, take proper care of them and do not abuse them by applying force they are not designed to take. Vices and adjustable wrenches are all too often broken by applying a tube to obtain increased leverage. The use of die nuts instead of stocks and dies when cutting threads is also mistaken.

Common user tools are apt to be left where they were last used, often outside where they quickly rust and cannot be found when next wanted. A place for everything and insistence that everything is properly cleaned and put back in place after use is the answer to this.

Files, if treated properly will last for years; keep a new file for gunmetal which demands a keen cutting edge. When a file becomes too dull for this purpose it will be just right for cast iron and when it will no longer cut cast iron it can be finished up on mild steel.

Do not use any file on a case hardened surface as this will blunt the teeth in no time. For this reason the good mechanic keeps his files in a drawer, separated from each other by a wooden partition to avoid rubbing and blunting their teeth.

Frequent brushing with a file card or scratch brush to remove small metallic particles from the teeth, which if not removed, will produce scratches on the work, will keep the file in good condition. Some old time mechanics even applied this principle to taps and dies, keeping a separate set for gunmetal.

Chisels too, should be kept with a keen cutting edge. In skilled hands a chisel is a precision tool and in days gone by a man skilled in the art of chipping and filing could produce a plane surface equal almost to that of a shaping machine and often as quickly, for instance, when closing big end brasses.

Lifting appliances

Two hydraulic jacks of 25 to 30 tons capacity and an adequate supply of baulks or sound sleepers will cater for such contingencies as spring changing, removal of wheels and derailments.

A Yale 'Pullift' or 10 cwt chain blocks are a convenience for lifting cylinder covers, blast pipes and other heavy items.

'Pullift'. The Yale-Townend 'Pullift' is a lightweight winch made in three capacities, $\frac{3}{4}$, $1\frac{1}{2}$ and 3 tons for lifting or hauling. It consists of a hand lever operated reversible crab engaging with some ten feet of motor cycle chain which is made to travel in and out of the winch at will. There are of course hooks at each extremity.

'Tirfor' Winch. This is another most useful appliance. It works on the same principle but uses instead of a motor cycle chain, about 50ft of thin wire rope. This is invaluable for hauling a dead engine in and out of its shed or when suspended from a roof truss, lifting connecting rods etc., from its bunker.

GLAND PACKING

There are numerous glands or stuffing boxes on a locomotive ranging from small cocks with a spindle having the diameter of a pencil for which a few turns of asbestos string will suffice to make steam tight, to those of large diameter ($3\frac{1}{2}$ inch) such as piston rods packed with metallic rings, where provision is made for the rod to 'float' in order to allow for wear on the crosshead and piston head.

Where movement is intermittent or occasional, graphited asbestos string or rope is appropriate and in certain modern applications, moulded asbestos rings with metallic insertions are used for packing regulator rods.

All old packing should be extracted before new is added, as it has a tendency to harden and grip the spindle especially the regulator glands which become coated with lime in districts with chalky water.

There is no short cut at present known to reduce the tedious labour of extracting old and hardened asbestos rope packing, especially from a regulator stuffing box, which may be some four inches in depth. A sharpened scriber makes a fairly effective implement for picking out the packing from small glands, but where asbestos rope is concerned, it is generally necessary to chop it into small pieces with a long and slender chisel before it can be hooked out with an implement like a fairly large screw driver with its end turned over and sharpened.

When repacking small cocks with asbestos string, do not crowd in so much packing that there is barely sufficient thread to engage with the gland nut or its thread may be stripped when an attempt is made to force in the packing.

For the larger glands packed with asbestos rope, such as the piston rod and valve spindle glands of many industrial locomotives, opinions differ as to how this should be done. One school favours a series of separate rings arranged so that the joints (which should be as close as possible) are staggered in order to avoid a direct blow through of steam. Others favour a coil of four or five turns of rope (which may have to be flattened slightly by hammering before it can be wound in). This method has the merit of easier extraction once the end has been found and started; however unless great care is taken to taper the ends and to see that these are in line with one another like the tapered ends of a coil spring, the gland when tightened will have a tendency to tilt and score the rod. Particular care should, therefore, be taken when screwing up flanged glands to see that the annular clearance is equal throughout. Whichever method is adopted, additional packing subsequently introduced should be in the form of individual rings.

Old packing can sometimes be blown out of spindle and piston glands by giving the engine steam, after first removing the gland from its studs but there is the risk that, should the engine move or slip, the gland and its studs are most likely to be trapped and broken.

Metallic packing

The valve spindle and piston glands of most saturated steam railway locomotives are kept steam tight by spring and steam loaded conical white metal alloy packing rings contained in a vibrating cup which is free to adjust itself to any up and down movement of the piston rod.

These alloy rings wear extremely well and impart a high polish to their respective rods or spindles. Unlike the rope packed variety they do not score or corrugate the rod. Being soft and of conical shape, the pressure of steam will gradually squeeze the first or conical ring, through the vibrating cup, from which it will be extruded as a paper thin film.

When worn out, new packing rings bored to a diameter slightly less than that of the rod so that they grip the rod without dropping off, should be fitted.

Cast iron packing

This originated on the former North Staffordshire Railway under its last CME, (Mr Hookham) and is extensively used on superheated steam locomotives where the ordinary white metal rings tend to melt under high temperatures. When well lubricated, cast iron packing has a long life, but should the lubrication be inadequate or intermittent, the packing will be rapidly torn out and the rod scored.

There are two main types of cast iron packing – the original design in the shape of a horseshoe with a smaller segment between the jaws, kept in close contact with the rod by a strong semicircular clip spring, and those made up of three interlocking segments encircled by a coiled spring (Hühn and Britimp).

When new, $\frac{1}{8}$ inch 'draw' is allowed between the segments but as wear takes place, this diminishes to nothing. A further lease of life can be given to the packing by filing $\frac{1}{8}$ inch off the jaws of the smaller segment, but experience has shown that once the bore of the packing has become enlarged, it is difficult to restore to a steam tight condition even with careful bedding. The most satisfactory solution is to fit new packing rings, boring them out so as to grip the rod tightly.

Whichever type of packing is fitted, whether white metal or cast iron, it cannot be expected to remain steam tight for long if there is 'lift' on the crosshead, the piston neck rings are a slack fit, or the piston rod is worn with ridges at the

Woodham Bros scrapyard at Barry in South Wales has been the source of numerous locomotives acquired for preservation and restoration. The condition of boiler, frames and cylinders has had to be considered in determining which locomotives were worth restoration without costs of the project rising beyond unacceptable limits. Even with voluntary labour, the purchase price, transport costs, and such new materials as superheater tubes and replacement non-ferrous fittings, have put even basic standard gauge steam locomotive restoration costs in the £10,000–£20,000 range in recent years. *Above* is a line of locomotives at Barry, and *left* a close view of a cylinder and bogie of an LMS Class 5 4-6-0 showing some of the problems that await the preservationist. (*G. T. Heavyside*)

extremities of its working stroke. The remedy here is to refit the crosshead and renew the neck ring bushes and turn or grind the piston rod.

JOINTMAKING

It is a well proved engineering axiom that the 'best joint is no joint at all'; in other words, it is a metal to metal joint.

Nearly all small pipe joints are like this, whether of the older type where a conical nipple is brazed on to the pipe or the modern variety incorporating a double coned sleeve or 'olive' that is a good sliding fit on the pipe to be jointed. In both instances the cone end or 'olive' is forced into a conical recess by tightening a union nut or flange.

The latter type, usually referred to as an 'Air Ministry joint', was originally developed for aircraft pipe work and was extensively used on the LNER for injector and other pipes. It had the advantage that brazing was avoided; all that was necessary was to anneal and bell out the end of the copper pipes to be connected to receive the barrel shaped 'olive'.

Large pipes, such as main steam pipes, are flanged and whether jointing is used or not, *must be faced up dead flat* to a surface plate; likewise the mating surface on cylinder or tube plate. The periphery of the flange outside the stud or bolt holes should be *relieved* or 'backed off' in order that the load may be concentrated within the area encompassed by the bolt holes.

Thin 'Golden Walkerite' or other reputable steam jointing should be used, the thinner the better as, should it blow out, the escape of steam will be less – hence the advantage of the metal to metal joint, but this is time consuming and therefore costly to produce.

A modern development is the 'lens' joint – a lens shaped steel ring, sometimes flat on one surface, that is a ground-in fit to both steam pipe and casting. The 'Melesco' ball-ended superheater element joint is similar in principle. Both are self adjusting and need no jointing.

Large joints like cylinder, or steam chest covers are faced metal to metal when new, but when corroded and distorted with age a 'Hulburd' copper joint ring is often used. This can be annealed over and over again (ie, heating to a cherry red and plunging into cold water) but has the disadvantage that corrosion and pitting of the cylinder face occurs through electrolytic action

between copper and iron in the presence of moisture and sulphurous smokebox ash.

Dome and manhole cover joints on boilers are generally made with 1 mm 'Walkerite' jointing, although 'Hulburd' copper joint rings are sometimes used.

It is good practice when making the larger joints (other than the copper ring type) to smear the mating surfaces with cylinder oil or graphite grease. Not only will this preserve the faces but will assist in breaking the joint at a subsequent repair.

Do *not* be persuaded to use any of the various metallic cements on the market as a jointing compound. They are certainly effective in stopping blows, but their use will be regretted when the time comes to remove a cylinder or dome cover, especially if the jointing has been squeezed into the stud holes and has to be laboriously chipped away from the base of the threads of studs after wedging off the cover.

Some companies provided for this purpose a tapped hole in the cover, into which a set or 'jacking' screw could be screwed for breaking the joint.

Dome joints

The safe way of lifting off the sheet steel casing or 'bonnet' covering the dome proper of a tender engine, is for the fitter and his assistant to stand on the hand rails facing each other with knees braced against the boiler barrel.

Lifting together, the 'bonnet' is raised clear of the dome and then lowered into a convenient place on the barrel, leaving sufficient room for the much heavier dome cover or manhole joint that is to follow. The stud on the dome cover for securing the 'bonnet' will prevent it from sliding when it is turned over for cleaning the joint face.

In order to ensure that this or any other cover is replaced in precisely the same position, mark with a chisel, the front with a letter F, or T for top, R or L as the case may be.

ADJUSTMENT OF BEARINGS

Some railway companies provided adjustable wedges to take up wear between the axlebox and its guide or hornblock, others did not. A wedge kept in proper adjustment will maintain an engine in good riding condition for a longer period than one without wedges; on the other hand, if neglected the resultant 'knock' or pounding is infinitely worse than with worn plain parallel horns.

In recent years the fitting of hard manganese liners to parallel horns has so reduced the amount of wear that there is no longer the necessity to provide means of adjustment, consequently there is no wedge to drop and cause excessive knock.

Axlebox wedges

With a pinch bar, pinch each pair of coupled wheels in turn against the fixed face of the horn and slacken the side locking bolt of the wedges, also the vertical adjusting screw lock nuts.

Next, prise the wedge upwards with a short tommy bar or screw it upwards with moderate force using a short spanner; then, noting the position of the wedge relative to the horn, drop it $\frac{1}{4}$ inch, or two complete turns of the adjusting nut to give the necessary working clearance.

Measure the clearance between the axlebox and wedge with a long feeler of 15 to 20 thou thickness. (A length of clock spring straightened out makes quite a good feeler). This is most important for apart from heating **a seized axlebox is liable to cause derailment.**

Finally, tighten and secure the adjusting nuts and lock bolt not overlooking the security of the hornstay, for it is this component that takes the downward thrust of the wedge.

Split brasses

The practice of allowing 'draw' on split brasses by using the tapered cotter as a means of adjustment was abandoned many years ago because of the tendency of the cotter to be flung out at high rates of rotation.

No 'draw' is permitted nowadays, brasses are closed to a running clearance of one thou per inch diameter, either with a file or on a shaping machine until a pair of inside calipers, set accurately to the *maximum* diameter of the crank pin, has a swing of $\frac{3}{4}$ inch to one inch between the brasses of an inside cylinder engine at their *smallest* diameter.

The strap and brasses are then reassembled on the crank pin, cottered down solid and tested for freedom of rotation by spinning the whole assembly on the crank pin; it should do so freely but without any shake. It may then be reconnected to its connecting rod, the cotter being secured against movement by its set screws and a split cotter, bearing hard against the strap.

Method of taking down the strap type big ends of inside cylinder engines

Place the engine over a pit and set the big end to be taken down on the bottom quarter, slacken the cotter retaining set screws and take out the main cotter.

Remove the split pins from the big end bolts and slacken the lock and main nuts two or three turns and lock securely one against the other.

A heavy hammer, 7 to 14 lb in weight, with a short shaft, is required to drive out the long taper fitting bolts, but *not* directly on the nipple end, for the energy of the blow will be absorbed uselessly in crushing the pinhole and bend the bolt.

The tool that is needed is a steel cup that bears against the two locked nuts, with a hole in it to relieve the pressure on the nipple; such a cup usually has a stout wire or wicker handle attached to it so that it can be held in position by an assistant.

The best way of swinging a heavy hammer upwards is to use it like a croquet mallet only with considerably more force! The act of bending down to grasp the short shaft will bring the wrists in contact with the knees which are used to impart an upward motion as the back is straightened. When hit fairly and squarely the impact can be felt as well as heard; with practice you will be able to tell whether you are striking true or not.

Bolts that have become shouldered through hydraulic pressure take a lot of shifting; it used to be said that a bolt was not really tight until it had to be drilled out! The bolts having been removed, the strap can now be prised off the rod and allowed to fall on to a piece of wood placed in the pit ready to receive it. The connecting rod is then prised forward to release the front brass and cotter block and secured to the weigh bar shaft by a stout rope or chain passed through the opening in its butt end.

Re-erection is performed by reversing this process except that the strap with back brass in position is raised by two men.

One man with his back to the firebox uses the oil well to lift by, while the man in front thrusts a chisel into the cotter way as a purchase. As soon as the top bolt holes in the strap are raised clear of the crank pin, insert a bolt. The strap now hangs safely while the bearing and journal are cleaned and oiled prior to turning over the strap in order to receive the front brass, shims, cotter block and cotter.

Now lock the strap into approximately its

ASSEMBLING A STRAPPED BIG END

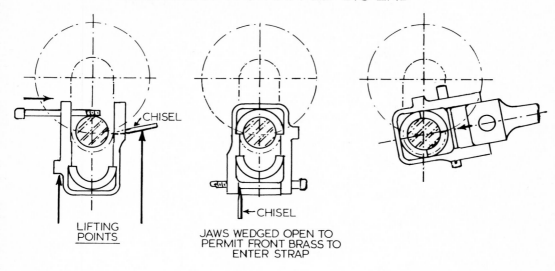

LIFTING POINTS

CHISEL

JAWS WEDGED OPEN TO PERMIT FRONT BRASS TO ENTER STRAP

←CHISEL

Fig 3. Assembling a strapped big-end on an inside cylinder locomotive.

correct position by tightening one of the cotter set screws against the crank web and prise the connecting rod towards it while your mate supports the butt end on his shoulder. Once fairly entered into the strap it can be slid into position, the bolts oiled, inserted and hammered home.

This is a much safer method than the alternative one of prising back the connecting rod so as to trap the front brass against the journal and then lifting up the strap and back brass bodily and sliding it on to the rod. However, this method is the best way of putting up the inside marine type big end of a Gresley three-cylinder engine but in this case, only the much lighter strap has to be lifted, the semi-circular back brass being held in position meantime by wedging it between the crank webs with two small 'fox' wedges that are subsequently removed.

As more and more heavy repairs are undertaken at preservation centres it will not be out of place to describe how a big end strap that has become slack on its rod, is re-fitted.

The heel of the strap is brought to forging heat and a stout cramp applied to close it in, using the cotter block and a wedge as a distance piece in order to keep it parallel.

The bearing faces are then filed parallel to one another and true to a surface plate, likewise the mating surfaces on the connecting rod butt end.

The strap should nip the rod at the heel but not at the jaw end, thus ensuring that when the bolts are tightened down the strap grips the rod tightly.

If a tapered bolt reamer is available the holes can be trued up and new bolts turned and fitted.

Do not forget to stamp on these their position, ie, R1, R2, etc, also the engine number. This saves time and temper later on when deciding where each of the four bolts belong – also to which engine!

A slightly worn bolt can often be given a new lease of life by turning off a little metal from the underside of its head. A bolt properly fitted can be driven to within $\frac{1}{8}$ inch of being home with a hand hammer.

Piston clearance

This is necessary in order that the pistons do not strike the cylinder covers at the end of their stroke. The method of ascertaining piston clearance is as follows:

Disconnect the connecting rod from the crosshead and prise the latter forward until the piston bumps against the front cylinder cover and mark this position of the crosshead on the slide bars, do the same for the back centre. Re-connect the connecting rod and repeat.

The distance between the two marks at each end of the slide bar is the piston clearance and should be approximately equal, the front clearances being slightly greater to allow for expansion of the piston rod when hot, also to allow for the engine settling down on its springs where the cylinders are inclined.

When split brasses are being closed or reduced on account of wear it is important to see that the piston clearances are not disturbed. Therefore, a shim or liner of the equivalent thickness to the metal removed from the jaw of the brass must be placed at the back of the brass to compensate.

A multiplicity of thin liners is objectionable as these are apt to be misplaced or lost and the piston clearances reduced to a dangerous extent.

The same care must be exercised when adjusting the coupling rod split brasses often found on industrial engines but in this case the added precaution must be taken of trammelling the distance between centres of the split brasses to ensure that these coincide with the axle centres if hot crank pins are to be avoided; alternatively, adjust the brasses when on the dead centres.

A good guide is the position of the oil hole in the rod relative to the split between the brasses, but this is approximate only.

VALVE AND PISTON RING RENEWAL

The method of testing valves and pistons for steam tightness has been described already and as long as these remain so, are better left undisturbed. The best recipe for a long life of valve and piston rings is regular lubrication and the avoidance of priming which washes off the lubricant from cylinder walls and causes more wear in a few hundred yards than thousands of miles of normal running.

Most modern engines have piston rods long enough to permit the piston heads to rest on the cylinder cover studs so that rings can be renewed with no disconnection other than removal of the gudgeon pin.

Unfortunately there are still in existence engines where it is necessary to remove the piston head from the rod before the rings can be reached; these have the crosshead (or part of it) forged solid with the piston rod as in marine practice.

When the cylinder has been opened up, it should be carefully examined for wear and cracks.

An oily surface does not necessarily mean good lubrication. Some of the BR Standard classes were notorious for tearing out their piston rings and scoring cylinders. Rings often became deep blue with heat, and the steam passages, instead of being black, were white from lime deposit caused by water carried over into the cylinders.

The piston head should next be examined to see that it is securely on its rod and that there are no cracks radiating from its boss. If there is a gap between the nut and piston head, this is conclusive proof that the head has been driven up on the cone end by hydraulic pressure. It must then be withdrawn and refitted, taking care to see that the piston clearance at the back is not dangerously reduced.

A loose piston head can be detected when the engine is moving slowly in steam by a loud report like a pistol shot on the forward stroke and a muffled bang on the return stroke. Once heard and recognised, it will never be mistaken for a knocking big end.

Once the piston head and cylinders are in good order, the crosshead can then be levered forward until the piston head is almost clear of the cylinder when the rings can be removed – unless, as sometimes happens, they have disintegrated and drop out like a handful of marbles!

Next examine the ring grooves in the piston head. If the rings have broken up this is often due to the grooves' wearing taper causing slackness and hammering of the relatively fragile ring. The remedy here is to remove the piston, skim out the grooves parallel in a lathe and fit oversize rings.

If the gap between piston head and the cylinder bore exceeds $\frac{1}{4}$ inch, it is high time that the head is renewed or restored by metal deposition.

The cylinder bore should next be measured for diameter and ovality. There is nothing that one can do about the latter short of re-boring, but it is useful to record for the future.

It will be assumed that rings for both pistons and valves will be obtained from a firm specialising in the manufacture of these components, probably for large diesel engines. When ordering **it is most important that a clear understanding be obtained as to whether it is the purchaser or the supplier who makes the allowance for compression.**

An explanation of how the 'Ramsbottom' spring piston ring is made will make this point clear. In order that the ring shall have spring or

Bogie of a Festiniog Railway Fairlie locomotive showing the steam and exhaust pipes, and valve chests. (*Festiniog Railway*)

compression it is made somewhat larger in diameter than the cylinder it is to fit. It is then cut diagonally and pushed into the cylinder with the two ends overlapping. The amount of overlap will be 3 ½ times the difference in diameter between the cylinder bore and the quill from which the ring was made, eg a 20 inch diameter cylinder will require a ring, say $20\frac{3}{8}$ inch in diameter which, when gapped by the removal of $1\frac{1}{8}$ inch, will permit the ring to close by this amount when pushed into the cylinder.

Conversely a worn ring that has lost its compression will be the same diameter as the cylinder bore.

Allow a gap between the 'points' of the ring for expansion when hot of $\frac{1}{16}$ inch for saturated, and $\frac{1}{8}$ inch for superheated engines.

In order to avoid misunderstanding when ordering, tell the manufacturer that the cylinder bore is 'x' inches in diameter and he is required to supply a ring gapped and with the requisite compression to fit this diameter. He will also require to know the width and depth of the ring grooves in the piston head.

Ring stops

Piston valve heads and many pistons are provided with stops to prevent the rings from turning and springing into the steam ports. Should they do so, the ring will be broken and probably the rim of the valve head also.

The simplest form of stop is a round peg screwed into the ring groove; an improvement on this arrangement is one that serves two adjacent grooves, for not only does it stop the rings from turning but is itself prevented from unscrewing by these same rings. Piston head ring stops are frequenty a plain bar fitted diagonally across the groove.

Whatever the type of stop, it is important that the ring is properly fitted to it, otherwise the clearance for expansion will be destroyed with consequent seizure and damage to the motion. If the points of a diagonally cut valve ring do not pass one another when tried in the most worn part of the sleeve, (across the bridges) there is sufficient compression left in the ring for further services.

In an emergency, until new piston rings can be obtained, the old ones can be given a short extra term of life by 'peening' them lightly on the inside with the ball peen of a light hammer, using the rail as an anvil.

SPLITTING PISTONS AND CROSSHEADS

The security of a piston rod in its crosshead depends mainly on the friction between the surfaces of the coned joint and to a lesser extent on the sheer strength of the tapered cotter that draws it into the crosshead.

There are two methods of fitting, (a) with 'draw' used chiefly on slide valve engines, and (b) where 'no draw' is allowed and the piston rod bottoms solidly in the crosshead. This is the method used on most piston valve engines where the risk of damage by hydraulic pressure is much greater than is the case with a slide valve which, lifting from its face, will allow an excess of pressure in the cylinder to escape.

Piston rods can be separated from their crossheads in two ways, for those with 'draw' by means of a button and wedge and for those without, by a hydraulic ram; in either case much greater force is needed to separate the rod from its crosshead than to drive it in.

These appliances are used as follows:

Button and wedge
1. Disconnect the small end of the connecting rod from the crosshead.
2. Place a hardened steel 'button' in the hole in the crosshead that exposes the end of the piston rod. This 'button' will vary in size and shape according to the design of the engine; on some it will be broad and flat like a button, on others it will resemble more closely a cotton reel.
3. Replace the gudgeon pin, first slipping on it an old small end bush or half brass in order to protect its surface from damage when driving in the wedge.
4. Using a heavy hammer, drive a stout steel wedge with a slow taper between the button and the bush. A few good well placed blows should suffice to break the joint. If the wedge keeps flying out then its taper is too sharp.

In very stubborn cases it may be necessary to heat the boss of the crosshead in order to expand it and so loosen its grip on the rod.

Hydraulic ram
This is either anchored in the crosshead by the gudgeon pin or else is mounted in a strong stirrup engaging externally with the crosshead boss. By screwing in a pressure screw with a small ratchet handle, a pressure of up to 25 tons is exerted on the grease with which the ram is packed.

Damage caused by priming
When an engine that has 'got hold of the water' is examined it may well be found that either the

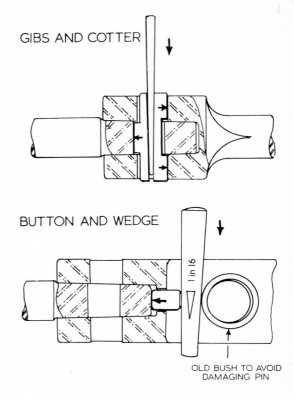

GIBS AND COTTER

BUTTON AND WEDGE

1 in 16

OLD BUSH TO AVOID DAMAGING PIN

Fig 4. The method of extracting piston valves with gibs and cotter, described in the paragraph, right. The lower diagram shows the button and wedge method to separate a piston rod from the crosshead as described on the left.

piston head or the crosshead joint has been loosened. The latter will be betrayed by the piston rod cotter dropping through the cotterway in the crosshead.

When the rod has been pulled outwards the cotter will be badly bent or partially sheared. When the piston cotter of an L1 class engine was sheared into three separate pieces, it was calculated that a force of 200 tons had been exerted.

The remedy in the case of the loose piston head is to drill out the taper pin securing the nut and to re-tighten it, first having fitted a washer of the requisite thickness in order to re-align the taper pin holes.

For a loose crosshead a broader cotter may suffice; if it does not, the a small amount of metal, possibly only $\frac{1}{32}$ inch, must be knifed off the end of the rod but care must be taken to ensure that 'draw' on the cotter is not destroyed or made negative in the process, nor the piston clearance at the back reduced unduly.

Extracting piston valves

Valve spindles are usually connected to their crossheads or to the intermediate valve spindles that act as guides by a tapered joint in the same way as a piston is secured. This joint can be broken in several ways either by using a button and wedge or if a tapped hole is provided in the crosshead by screwing in a jacking screw.

Neither of these methods can be applied to many older engines; then the only way to break the joint is to use the old fashioned 'gibs and cotters'. These are inherently weak in design and tend to bend instead of wedging the spindle and crosshead apart. The best results are obtained by making the gibs as broad and the cotter as narrow as possible and preferably of hardened steel.

Difficulty may be experienced in pulling a piston valve through the unworn portion of the sleeve due to an accumulation of carbon under the rings, which must be crushed before the valve can be withdrawn.

Applying a rotary motion to the end of the spindle will help but in bad cases it may be necessary to take down the motion and jack out the valve from the rear. The valve heads can be cleaned of carbon in a fire but take care not to overheat the cast iron head.

VALVE SETTING

The purpose of setting or adjusting valves is to equalise as far as possible the amount of steam admitted to each end of the cylinder so that the power impulses are both uniform and evenly spaced.

In the conventional steam locomotive the reciprocating motion of the piston is converted into a rotary movement at the wheel, which in turn drives the valve gear, so reversing the process by imparting a reciprocating motion to the valve governing the admission and exhaust of steam to and from the cylinder. This combination of motions produces 'angularity' and consequently a discrepancy in opening between the front and back ports; in other words the shorter the connecting rod the nearer the back cover is the piston when the big end is at half stroke (on its top or bottom quarters).

By careful design this effect can be reduced to a minimum by offsetting the angularity of one component against another, but a compromise is inevitable and every effort is made to give the best distribution at the normal running cut-off of the locomotive.

Tools required for valve setting

Two trammels (one short, one long)
Two pairs of dividers (three and eight inch, approximately).
Two centre punches (one fine, one heavy).
One steel rule, calibrated in 32nds inch.
One measuring staff about four feet long.

Trammels for valve setting were commonly made from old coil steel springs, of about $\frac{5}{16}$ inch round or square section and were L shaped with both extremities sharpened to a scriber point, the short leg being about three inches and the longer one of such a length as will reach from a fixed point (a centre punch dot) on the steam chest to a convenient position on the valve spindle or its connecting link, depending on the design of engine. A length of six to nine inches was quite common.

A second and longer trammel is required for marking the tyre of the wheel tangentially from a convenient fixed point on the engine frame, generally one of the platform brackets or underside of the platform.

The long leg of this trammel may be anything from 12 inches to 24 inches long, depending on the design of the engine.

Port measuring staff

This is required to gauge with accuracy the distance between the port edges of piston valve liners so that this can be compared with the distance the valve heads are apart.

In railway workshops quite elaborate and sophisticated measuring devices have been designed and made for this purpose but their manufacture is hardly justified at a preservation centre.

A four foot length of 'Dexion' or 'Handyangle', or comparable material, makes an excellent measuring staff if two of the triangular corner plates are attached at its extremities to engage in the steam ports.

The edges at right angles to the staff should face outwards when gauging the distance over the exhaust edges and inwards when gauging the steam edges. The slotted holes will permit a certain amount of adjustment in length.

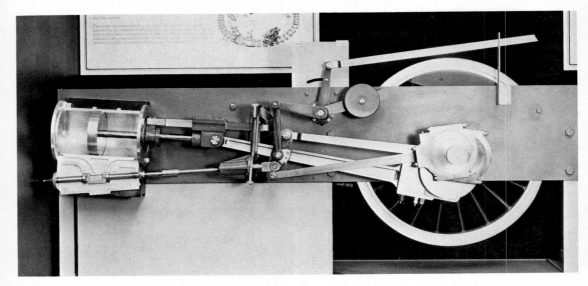

Stephenson's valve gear as depicted on a model of the GER Claude Hamilton arrangement. (*National Railway Museum*)

Stephenson's valve gear

First Operation: Transposing the points of admission/cut-off to the valve spindle. Example: a typical British shunting engine with Stephenson's gear actuating two slide valves in a narrow steam chest between the inside cylinders.

The first thing to do, when not certain of the amount of steam lap, is to remove both valves and their buckles (the rectangular frame embracing the valve) from the steam chest and compare the overall width of the valve and the width of the exhaust cavity, with the corresponding ports in the port face. An easy and accurate way of doing this is to take a rubbing of the port face on a sheet of paper and then place this centrally on the valve. It will be immediately apparent how much lap the valve has, also whether the exhaust edges are 'line on line', or if there is exhaust lap or clearance.

Keep this impression of the port face for future reference and record on it the dimensions of the valve, for with this knowledge, there will be no need to remove the valves for marking off on any future occasion.

Replace one valve in its buckle in the steam chest and using a piece of thin tin as a feeler, draw the valve forward until the piece of tin is trapped midway between the valve lap and the edge of the front port; this is the point of admission/cut-off

and taking care not to alter the position of the valve, scribe a line with the short trammel on the valve spindle (which should have been blackened previously with smoke from a flare lamp or candle to make the marks show up clearly).

Repeat for the back port by thrusting the arm well into the steam chest to reach the back port and mark the spindle afresh with the trammel. Now there are two scribed lines on the spindle exactly twice the valve lap apart and each should be lightly centre popped for reference. The front pop when immediately below the trammel point is the point of admission/cut-off for the front port and the pop at the rear for that of the back port. When the valve is moved so that the trammel point is mid-way between the two dots it is in its central position and both ports are closed to steam.

Now remove the valve just marked off and repeat for the other side, after which both can be put back and the steam chest cover replaced. By using the same trammel and the same reference pops, the position of either valve, although now hidden in the steam chest, can be ascertained at will.

If the valve lap is known the procedure just described is unnecessary; then there is no need to do more than remove the steam chest cover, the point of admission/cut-off at both front ports is visible without disconnection and, having marked the spindle with the trammel, the cut-off point of the back ports will be found at a distance of exactly twice the valve lap towards the rear.

Second Operation: 'Trying over the valves'
The first consideration is that adequate and controlled power is available for moving the engine slowly and steadily. For this purpose a Diesel shunter, tightly coupled to avoid jerks and snatches, is ideal.

In the absence of mechanical power the engine must be propelled with pinch bars, the greater the number that can be applied the less the effort required and the greater certainty of movement.

As level a piece of straight track as can be found without low rail joints to cause stalling should be selected, preferably with a pit if an inside cylinder engine is being dealt with.

Choice of methods
There are two principal methods of setting valves:

1. *By equalising the lead* involving 'quartering the wheel'. This is the most accurate method and is one generally adopted in the Main Works but has the disadvantage that the engine must be stopped with precision at frequent intervals.

2. *By equalising the port opening at the running cut-off.* This can be effected without stopping the engine, apart from reversing its direction of travel and is consequently the most convenient for use in a Running Shed.
   The second method will be described first.

Trammelling. Having set the reversing gear in forward gear at the working cut-off we are now ready to try over.

The sequence in which the ports open to steam in forward gear in a two-cylinder engine with the RH crank leading is:
RF, LF, RB, LB
The sequence is reversed when going backwards and by memorising the order of events, unnecessary movements of the engine can be avoided.

Using the same trammels as for marking off the points of cut-off and using the same datum point on the steam chest (chalk a ring round it so that it can be easily found), hold the short end of the

trammel ready poised above the valve spindle, previously blackened with soot. As soon as the centre punch pop, indicating the point of cut-off, has passed below the trammel point, commence scratching off the soot by passing and repassing the scriber point across the spindle and continue to do so until the spindle has stopped moving (maximum port opening) and starts to move back.

Taking the small dividers, place one point in the admission/cut-off centre punch pop and carefully adjust the other point until it is at the limit of the scratching on the spindle. Measure carefully and *record*; this is the port opening. Repeat and record for the other three events, then smoke the spindle afresh, put the engine in back gear and go through the procedure again, remembering, of course, that the engine must now move backwards.

Fig 5. The method of equalising port openings in a link motion, described on this page and related to the tables overleaf.

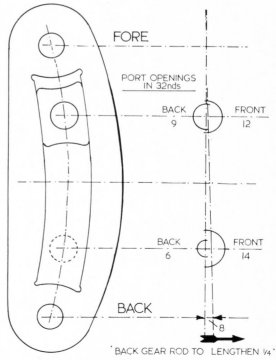

METHOD OF EQUALISING PORT OPENINGS IN A LINK MOTION

FORE

PORT OPENINGS IN 32nds

BACK 9   FRONT 12

BACK 6   FRONT 14

BACK

8

`BACK GEAR ROD TO LENGTHEN 1/4"

N.B PORT OPENINGS IN <u>BOTH</u> GEARS ARE NOW EQUAL

Readings. In order to avoid confusion and errors in calculating the alterations required, it is good practice to avoid fractions and to express all measurements in whole numbers either 64ths or 32nds of an inch, according to the accuracy required.

The following example is taken from a two cylinder narrow gauge engine, fitted with Stephenson's gear. (Readings in 32nd inches).

Before adjustment

| | L | | R | |
	Front Port	Back Port	Front Port	Back Port
FORE GEAR	12	9	11	14
BACK GEAR	14	6	8	8

The left back gear rod was then *lengthened* by $\frac{1}{4}$ inch or $\frac{8}{32}$nds and the right fore gear rod *shortened* by $\frac{1}{8}$ inch or $\frac{4}{32}$nds. The readings became:

After adjustment

| | L | | R | |
	Front Port	Back Port	Front Port	Back Port
FORE GEAR	11	11	12	12
BACK GEAR	10	9	9	6

It will be observed that the back gear port openings on the right side are no longer equal whereas the fore gear openings on the left side have become so, although neither of these rods was altered. This is due to the fact that as each rod is connected to opposite ends of the same link, one becomes the fulcrum point for the other and an alteration in the length of one will necessarily affect the distribution in *both* gears, but in varying degrees.

Alterations

The amount a rod must be lengthened or shortened is generally taken to be half the difference in port opening. This is approximately correct for an engine fitted with a marine type link where the eccentric rods are connected to lugs on the back of the expansion link. These have roughly the same amount of movement as the valve spindle die block in full gear, but it is certainly not the case with the locomotive type link pinned at top and bottom where the travel of the eccentric rod is approximately double that of

Fig 6. The method of marking an inside admission piston valve to obtain the admission cut-off points as described below.

the die block at running cut-off. It will be seen that this factor was taken into account when making the alterations to the example shown.

Alterations in the length of eccentric rods of engines fitted with Stephenson's valve gear are effected in two ways. In the forge, the rod can be shortened by 'jumping'. By the introduction of shims or liners of the requisite thickness between the eccentric strap and rod foot, the rod can be lengthened.

Walschaert's valve gear

This is an altogether much simpler gear to adjust for port openings. Slide valve engines frequently have a screw adjustment on the valve spindle; piston valve engines sometimes have this too but more often than not depend for adjustment on the thickness of a washer separating the valve head from the valve spindle collar. Such engines once put right seldom get out of adjustment except by wear in the motion and axleboxes.

The three-cylinder engines of the former LNER are readily adjustable by the introduction of thin steel 'buttons' about the size of a $\frac{5}{8}$ inch washer into the valve crossheads.

Another advantage of Walschaert's gear is that being directly connected to the valve spindle, the alteration necessary is always half the difference in port opening (neglecting an allowance for expansion when hot).

Occasionally faulty distribution with Walschaert's gear can be traced to a slight error in the angle of the return crank or length of an eccentric rod, but this is properly a job for the Main Works.

Piston valves

The method used for obtaining the admission/ cut-off points of a piston valve is much the same as for a slide valve, except that all the measurements are taken with a measuring staff or gauge.

The following are actual measurements taken from a famous locomotive equipped with inside admission piston valves designed with $1\frac{5}{8}$ inch lap

INSIDE ADMISSION PISTON VALVE

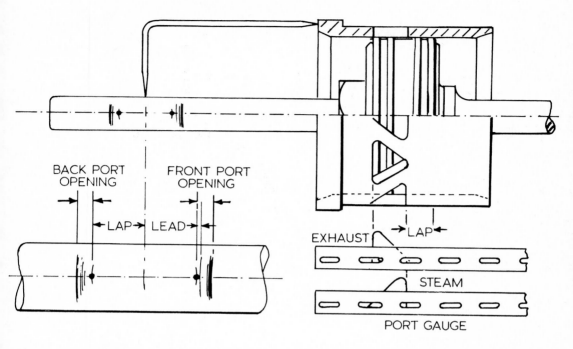

BACK PORT OPENING

FRONT PORT OPENING

LAP   LEAD

EXHAUST   LAP

STEAM

PORT GAUGE

and exhaust edges set 'line on line' ie, with neither exhaust lap nor exhaust clearance.

	Distance between	
	Steam Edges	Exhaust Edges
Ports in Liner	$25\frac{10}{32}$ inch	$28\frac{25}{32}$ inch
Valve Heads	22 inch	$28\frac{27}{32}$ inch
Difference divided by 2	$1\frac{21}{32}$ inch	$\frac{1}{32}$ inch
	lap*	lap*

* These discrepancies can be attributed to (a) a light deposit of carbon in the ports and (b) a slight inaccuracy in assembling the valve heads.

When dealing with the slide valve the point of reference was when the front port was just cracked open to steam; with inside admission piston valves it is when the front port is about to open to *exhaust* ie, when the valve is in its central position.

Now put a centre punch pop in the end of the valve liner (or any other convenient datum point), place the long end of the trammel in this and scribe a line on the spindle and centre pop. This is (or should be) the central position of the valve,

but in the example taken the valve has $\frac{1}{32}$ inch exhaust lap. Consequently the centre pop must be put that much *nearer* to the valve head so that when the trammel rests in this pop both exhaust rings cover their respective ports by an equal amount.

Now set the small dividers to $1\frac{21}{32}$ inch, ie, the *actual* steam lap and using the pop mark we have just made as the centre, describe two arcs on the spindle, one fore and one aft; these are the admission/cut-off points and each must be identified with a light centre pop.

It is now opportune to emphasise the essential differences in characteristics between an outside admission valve, such as a slide valve, and the inside admission variety, if confusion and errors are to be avoided when making adjustments.

An *outside admission* valve moves in the *same* direction as the piston at the commencement of its stroke and the front pop on the valve spindle is the admission/cut-off point for the front port and that at the rear for the back port. Consequently when in either of these positions, the valve is exactly the width of its lap from its central position.

An *inside admission* valve moves in the opposite direction to the piston at the commencement of its

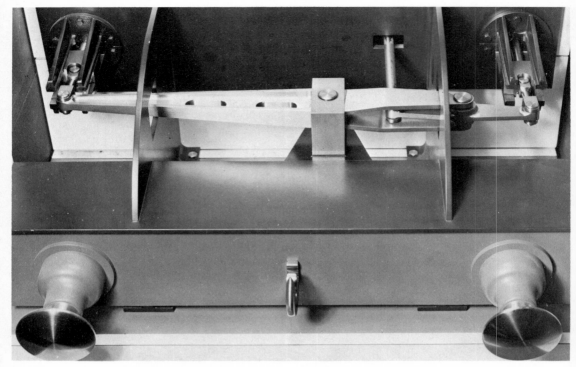

stroke and the *front* pop on the valve spindle is the admission/cut-off point for the *back* port and the rear mark for the *front* port.

Thermal expansion. A further factor to be considered is the allowance to be made for the lengthening of the valve spindle (and cylinder casting) when hot.

The text book allowance is .0000067 decimal parts of an inch, per inch of length, for every one degree Fahrenheit rise in temperature.

For small narrow gauge engines with short valve spindles using low pressure saturated steam, the amount the spindles expand when hot can be ignored; indeed a far more potent factor is wear in eccentric straps and axle boxes.

The effect of highly superheated steam at say 750°F on long valve spindles measuring perhaps 35 inches over exhaust edges, is quite another matter and expansion does materially affect steam distribution, especially at the front port.

What this allowance should be depends much on the design of the engine; a common allowance on slide valve engines is to allow $\frac{1}{16}$ inch greater opening at the front port, ie, the spindle will lengthen by $\frac{1}{32}$ inch so opening the back port and closing the front by this amount.

For highly superheated engines with long piston valve spindles, this amount could be doubled according to the practice of the workshops concerned. Some made no allowance for expansion, averring that, had the designers so intended, it would have been allowed in the valve setting tables.

Practice at Derby in the last days of steam was to allow $\frac{1}{16}$ inch for expansion, ie, the back port opening was $\frac{1}{8}$ inch greater than the front port with the valves set cold. The Doncaster allowance was half this amount.

Quartering the wheel: Setting by the lead. This is the usual method of setting valves on new engines of all types, also for re-setting valves on express engines working at a short cut-off.

The method of marking off, trammelling for port opening and subsequent adjustment is exactly the same as before; all that is different is that the port openings to steam, at the dead centres (the lead), are made equal (due allowance being made for expansion when hot).

Before describing the procedure for quartering the wheel ie, setting the crank accurately on its dead centres, a brief explanation of why it is done will help the student to appreciate the reason.

Left: A model of the Gresley two-to-one derived valve gear for three-cylinder engines. (*National Railway Museum*)

A reciprocating mechanism, whether it is for a piston or a valve, comes to rest and changes direction twice in every revolution of the wheel. In designing valve motions for steam engines advantage is taken of this useful characteristic by phasing the valve 90° or more apart from the piston that it controls.

This means that when the piston is stationary the valve is accelerating, thus giving a rapid opening to steam, and when the piston is moving fast the valve in its turn dwells, before moving rapidly to the point of cut-off.

It will be seen therefore that quite an appreciable angular movement of the crank will occur with hardly any perceptible movement of the piston, hence the need for quartering the wheel.

To set on the dead centres. Move the engine until a crosshead is within say half an inch of the end of its stroke and placing a square across the slide bar scribe a line across both crosshead and slide bar; then mark the tyre of the wheel, using the long trammel located in a centre pop on some convenient frame member, a bracket preferably at a tangent to the tyre.

Below: A close view of the sectioned right-hand cylinder and outside admission piston valve of rebuilt Merchant Navy 4-6-2 No 35029 *Ellerman Line* at the National Railway Museum. (*J. Edgington*)

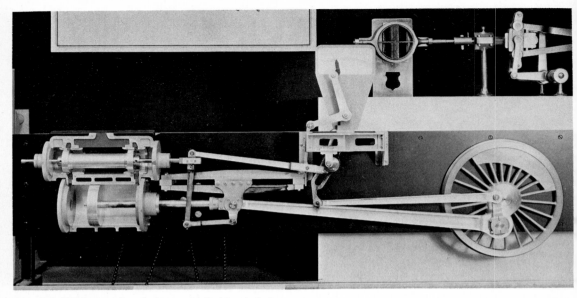

A model of Walschaert's valve gear with inside admission
piston valves. (*National Railway Museum*)

Now move the engine until the crank pin has
passed over its dead centre and the crosshead has
returned to its original position, mark the tyre
afresh and bisect the distance between the two
marks and centre pop heavily. This is the true
dead centre and by moving the engine back until
the trammel point rests in this centre pop it will
then be set accurately at zero degrees.

Chalk a ring round this mark for easy location
and identify it RF, LF, RB, LB as the case may be.

Taking the short trammel scribe an arc on the
valve spindle; its distance from the admission/cut-
off pop is the lead.

Repeat for the other dead centres, either four,
six or eight, according to the number of cylinders
and disposition of the cranks.

Having found all the dead centres and lead
openings, the engine may now be moved without
stopping, to obtain first the port openings in full
gear and then at the running cut-off, taking care
not to start scratching the spindle until the lead
mark is well clear.

It will be readily appreciated that pinch bars on
indifferent track are not ideal tools for this duty,
hence the more common method employed in
Running Sheds of equalising port openings at the
running cut-off.

In the main works, power operated jiggers were
used for rotating the wheels; frequent starting
and stopping was therefore no problem and it was
easy to compare the valve events, throughout
their range with the drawing office valve setting
table. On express engines, it was usual to verify
the actual point of cut-off by measuring the
piston's displacement from its dead centre for
both instroke and outstroke.

The method just described is particularly suited
to engines with Stephenson's or Allan's link
motion, where the lead increases as mid-gear is
approached, and the influence of one eccentric
diminishes as the other increases.

Lost motion in bearings. It is good practice to
make all scriber marks with the engine moving in
one direction only; when it is necessary to come
back to a mark as in quartering the wheel, go past
it and then return, thereby reducing the effect of
wear and play in motion and connecting rod
bearings.

Walschaert's valve gear: Proving the mid-gear position

Disconnect the eccentric rod from the
expansion link; also the union link from the
combination lever on the side to which the
reversing rod is connected.

Set the gear approximately in its mid position

and then rock the expansion link to and fro by hand, when the combination lever will be seen to swing like a pendulum. Get an assistant to adjust the reversing gear until this movement ceases and the combination lever is stationary.

The gear is now set accurately in mid position and the position of the sector plate should be altered to correspond. By repeating on the opposite side, any twist in the weigh shaft will be disclosed.

Errors in the length of the eccentric rod and angle at which the return crank is set, can be detected as follows. Set the big end on the side to be tested on either the front or back, dead centre, in the manner already described. Reverse the gear from full forward to full backward gear and observe whether the valve spindle remains stationary or moves in or out. Repeat for the opposite dead centre.

If the valve spindle remains stationary when the gear is reversed from one direction to the other on *both* dead centres, then the length of the eccentric rod and setting of the return crank is correct.

If the valve spindle moves in the same direction when the gear is reversed on both dead centres then the eccentric rod is at fault. A movement outwards indicates that the eccentric rod is too long, inwards that it is too short. If, however, when the gear is reversed on both dead centres, the movement of the valve spindle is in *opposite* directions then the angle at which the return crank is set is wrong.

A combination of these two errors will produce a greater movement on one dead centre than the other; first one and then the other error must be eliminated.

Stephenson's gear – Die block clearance

This should be approximately the same, in full forward and full backward positions of the gear.

A simple way of ascertaining this clearance is to knead some fireclay into a stiff dough and place a lump at the bottom of the expansion link and another at the top. Now move the engine one full turn and carefully remove the clay, the thicknesses will show the minimum amount of die block clearance.

Adjustment is usually made by altering the length of the reversing rod or, on some engines, by putting collars of appropriate thickness on the reversing screw on either side of the reversing screw die nut.

RESTORATION

The cost of restoring a locomotive to working order obviously will depend on its condition when acquired by the purchaser.

Ex BR locomotives bought from scrapyards have usually had all valuable bronze fittings and copper piping removed, and costly forgings, like coupling and connecting rods, are apt to be found burnt through with a cutting torch.

To restore such a machine to working order would cost many times its purchase price unless the prospective owners can call on exceptional skills or financial resources from among any group of supporters. Conversely, many industrial locomotives were working up to the time of their acquisition, although perhaps in a run-down condition. Provided the boiler is sound (and this is the key factor) very little work will be needed to restore such an engine to working order.

The commonly held notion that an engine must be pulled to pieces before it can be made fit to work is mistaken; all that is necessary as far as the mechanism is concerned is to overhaul the lubrication system thoroughly, clean out oil wells and renew trimmings. Any knocks or blows there are will be detected as soon as the engine is steamed and can be rectified subsequently.

I have put four standard gauge locomotives into running order, none of which had worked for about ten years, with no other attention than that described above, apart from pouring a gallon or so of fuel and cylinder oil down the blast pipe and giving this time to loosen any rust present in the cylinders. It is good policy to 'let well alone'. When it *is* necessary to strip an engine, make sure that all the various bits and pieces are restored to their proper places; eg, crank pin caps and their respective taper pins should be put back on the crank pins from whence they came.

Remove nuts from cylinder covers and other joints in a methodical manner and thread these and their washers on a piece of wire or string so that they can be replaced on the studs to which they belong. Haphazard replacement of nuts usually ends up with the tightest one being in the most awkward place. A lack of method often causes much time and energy to be wasted in searching for missing components and making replacements.

When driving in taper pins, split cotters and the like, have consideration for the person who, one day, will have to extract them – it may well be you. If there is a choice of direction, fit them so

that they can be driven out easily.

Take care when working in a smokebox to plug or cover securely all apertures leading to the cylinders, eg, a bolt falling unnoticed down a blast pipe can cause costly and perhaps irreparable damage to the cylinder casting and motion as the engine moves.

Removal of driving wheels

When removing or replacing a pair of driving wheels of an inside cylinder locomotive, only the absolute minimum of disconnections should be made in order to permit the driving wheel assembly (complete with springs if possible) to be rolled out.

Stripping and assembly of the crank axle can be done much quicker and better on the level than under the engine.

Disconnect as follows:
1. Connecting rods from big end straps.
2. Eccentric rods from eccentric straps.
3. Spring hangers (and springs depending on the design).
4. Hornstays.
5. Lubricator pipes.

After disconnection, connecting rods should be prised forward, raised clear and secured in order that they may not foul the wheels when they are rolled out. Big end straps should be secured against accidental rotation by unscrewing and locking between the crank webs one of the cotter retaining set screws.

Particular care should be taken to replace and secure on their respective studs any loose shims or liners introduced for altering the length of eccentric rods; **failure to do this will upset the valve setting.**

Re-metalling. From time to time it becomes necessary to re-metal a bearing on account of wear or heating. This process is not unduly difficult provided that adequate lifting and heating appliances are available; handling when hot a massive coupled axlebox, weighing perhaps 2cwt is no easy task, especially when heating has to be done in a smith's hearth.

Left: An underside view of the big ends and eccentrics and the spring nests of SECR 4-4-0 No 737 at the National Railway Museum, York. (*National Railway Museum*)

Assuming that lifting and heating facilities are available, proceed as follows: insert a stretcher bolt between the jaws of the axlebox to prevent them closing in, heat until any white metal remaining melts and runs out, then thoroughly wire brush the serrations or pockets and tin with tinman's solder, using killed spirits as a flux.

Meanwhile, sufficient white metal of the correct grade (tin base for locomotives, lead base for coaches and wagons) should be melting in a ladle. Take care to see that it is not overheated or the tin content will be burnt out so that the resulting metal will feel hard and gritty when scraped.

In the absence of a pyrometer, a rough guide to temperature is to dip a strip of good quality note paper into the molten metal, if it singes to a deep yellow or brown the temperature is about right, but if it ignites the metal has been spoiled.

The temperature of both bearing and molten metal being correct, pouring can commence. As the metal solidifies in the pockets, more must be added until it is proud, or above the level of the surrounding brass; the surplus can be removed, while still plastic, by wiping the surface of the metal with a hammer shaft or length of broom handle smeared with tallow or grease.

In days gone by, when running sheds had fewer

Below: Fitting an axlebox so that it beds correctly usually needs work with files, scrapers and blue marking. In this instance, at the Dart Valley Railway, a hoist suspended from sheer legs will be used to lift the axlebox into position. (*J. R. Besley, courtesy Dart Valley Railway*)

AXLEBOXES

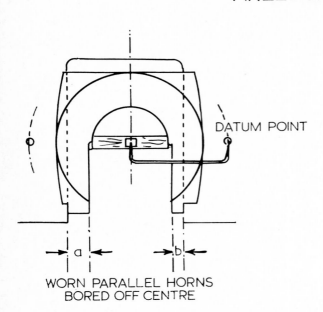

DATUM POINT

WORN PARALLEL HORNS
BORED OFF CENTRE

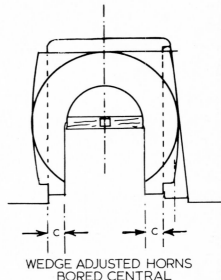

WEDGE ADJUSTED HORNS
BORED CENTRAL

machine tools and those that they had were otherwise engaged, it was common practice to hand-fit bearings; a man skilled in the art of white metalling could save a fitter a great deal of time. Not only were bearings hand fitted, but journals if not too badly scored, were filed true to calipers and a straight edge and were finally polished by two sheets of emery cloth encircled by a couple of turns of spun yarn pulled to and fro. Surprising as it may seem to a generation unaccustomed to such methods, bearings thus dealt with seldom ran hot if properly run in or seasoned.

The method just described is not applicable to the modern, serrated bearing and for this a form of chill is needed, usually a piece of thin sheet steel bent to the correct curvature, clamped to the bearing and smeared with graphite to prevent the molten metal from adhering. In this case, the bearing must be laid flat on its side, on a piece of steel plate and the metal poured in axially; when cool such bearings are bored to size in a lathe or boring mill.

Marking off axleboxes for boring. Coupled axleboxes that have wedge adjustment to take up wear are bored central, ie, the vertical centre line bisects the distance between the jaws or unworn part where the keep fits.

Where no axlebox wedges are provided as in

GWR and LMS practice, datum studs are affixed to the engine frame. Bisecting the distance between these points will give the true position of the axle centre relative to the front and rear horn faces. Wear will cause these distances to become unequal and axleboxes are then said to be bored off centre.

The centres so obtained are then transferred to the axlebox either directly, by positioning it in the horns, or on a surface table with a scribing block, using as a temporary centre a stick of wood about $1\frac{1}{4}$ inch square fitted tightly across the bore, to which, at its mid-point, is tacked a small square of tinplate with the four corners bent down. This provides a suitable surface on which to scribe and centre pop the vertical and horizontal centre lines.

From this centre a large circle is scribed on the face of the axlebox to assist in centering it accurately on the lathe face plate.

The position of the horizontal centre line will be determined by the axlebox crown thickness and whether there are bronze bars containing oil grooves; if so, these should make contact with the journal, otherwise they may become blocked by the softer white metal squeezing into them.

Boring of axleboxes. Difficulty will be experienced in measuring the bore of any bearing where the bearing area is less than half its diameter. So that it may not nip the journal, the bearing area of a locomotive axlebox does not greatly exceed 160°.

For this reason many railway turners made for themselves a set of radius gauges from thin plate, increasing in diameter by increments of $\frac{1}{32}$ inch. Even for a one off job it will pay to make such a gauge. Much unnecessary work with the file and bearing scraper will be avoided thereby.

After boring to size, the axlebox is then moved towards the lathe centre by $\frac{5}{8}$ inch and then counter-bored to a slightly larger diameter, this will provide the necessary backing off to give a 160° bearing.

Fitting axleboxes. Unless the machining has been so precise as to eliminate the need for fitting, it is customary to bed the axlebox on to its journal with the aid of files, scrapers and blue marking.

At some sheds a small crane which could be clamped to the wheel spokes was used to lift the heavy axleboxes on and off the journal during the bedding-in process. More commonly, the fitter had to improvise his own appliance and to utilise readily available articles.

First the wheels were securely scotched, then a pinch bar was thrust between the spokes of both wheels next to the rim at '4 o'clock' relative to a clock face; this bar formed a fulcrum for a strong plank about seven feet long, the opposite end of which rested on a stout trestle placed at '8 o'clock', relative to the pinch bar. On this plank which served both as a lever and a bridge, was placed the axlebox which could be easily rolled on and off the journal if an old pin or bush was interposed between it and the plank.

Once on the journal the plank was slid aside to permit the axlebox being rocked to and fro to obtain its marking. This process was reversed when removing the axlebox from the journal.

It was then rolled back over the trestle and tipped up to enable the fitter to remove the high spots on the bearing.

A useful tip when dealing with a pocketed bearing or one that has brass bars is first to

Left: Fig 7. Marking off axleboxes for boring, as described below left.

Below: Fig 8. Method of bedding axleboxes where lifting gear is not readily available, as described above.

METHOD OF BEDDING AXLEBOXES

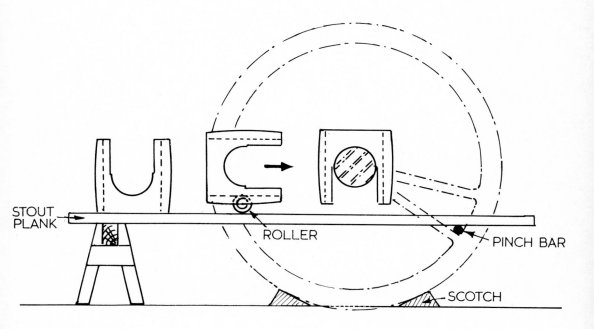

STOUT PLANK — ROLLER — PINCH BAR — SCOTCH

remove carefully with a $\frac{5}{8}$ inch square file, the tool marks in the brass area; this will leave the softer white metal slightly proud, consequently easier and quicker to bed down.

Finally draw a worsted trimming through all the oil holes and grooves in order to remove every particle of filings before replacing the axlebox on its journal, which should be well smeared with oil.

Slidebar alignment

When rebuilding an engine and before putting in the pistons, it is important to see that the slide bars are accurately aligned with their respective cylinders, otherwise excessive friction and wear will result.

Accurate alignment is achieved by setting the slide bar(s) parallel to and at the correct distance from the centre line of the cylinders. A strong nylon thread is stretched between two temporary brackets, one fastened to the front cylinder face and the other to the motion plate or other convenient point.

The front bracket locating the line at the centre of the cylinder consists of a strip of steel about a foot long attached at one end to a stud on the cylinder face and pierced at the other end with a $\frac{1}{16}$ inch diameter hole *exactly* at the cylinder centre through which the nylon line is threaded and tied to the loop of a $\frac{1}{8}$ inch diameter split pin. This line is drawn taut by hanging a weight on its remote end and adjusting its position until it is exactly in the centre of the gland stuffing box as measured with inside calipers.

In the case of two and four bar crossheads, the bottom bars are set first by adjusting the thickness of the shims at each end; the top bars are then set parallel to the lower ones.

The bottom bars of four bar crossheads are more easily set with a gauge instead of calipers. A gauge made from a piece of thin plate, in width half the thickness of the slipper blocks and spanning both bars, will facilitate this operation.

THE SMOKEBOX

Before starting work in a smokebox, give the upper half of the wrapper plate a good hammering from the outside in order to fetch down the worst of the soot and flaking rust which can then be swept up and shovelled out.

Provided the floor of the smokebox is level with the door, it can be hosed out clean with high pressure water to advantage but not when it is below, owing to the difficulty in getting rid of the water. Hosing will dislodge the soot and scale that accumulates on top of the superheater header.

An old sack to kneel on and a sweat rag or scarf worn round the neck will reduce the discomfort of working in a smokebox. If your skin grazes easily, wear gloves, for the interior of a smokebox is dry and rough and a glancing blow, which on oily motion would cause only a slight bruise will, in a smokebox, remove the skin. Having prepared, now start stripping the smokebox for, say, re-tubing.

The first item to remove is the crossbar to which the door is fastened, then the chimney cowl or petticoat together with vacuum exhaust, blower ring etc, followed by the blast pipe and, depending on design, the steam pipes. Apply plenty of penetrating oil to all the nuts that have to be removed and give this time to soak in.

Stout box spanners and a long bar together with short 'slogging' spanners (open jaw spanners cut in two) that can be struck with a 4 lb hammer are the tools for a smokebox job and, most important, a sharp flat chisel for splitting those nuts that defy all efforts to remove them with a spanner.

The secret of success in splitting nuts rests in the quality of the chisel; it must be finely drawn out and correctly tempered for if it is too hard it will break and if too soft it is useless. The art consists of driving the chisel downward through one of the flats of the nut taking care to keep it at all times parallel to the axis of the thread of the bolt or stud without damaging the threads. When nearly cut through, the chisel can be applied at right angles to the nut in order to break it apart.

Brass dome or cap nuts are sometimes encountered. They are very good for protecting the thread of a stud but tend to waste away and cause a box spanner to slip over the corners of the hexagon; they are also more difficult to split cleanly.

The modern alternative to splitting nuts is to burn the nut and bolt through with an oxy-acetylene cutting torch. This saves much time and skin but it is as well to know how to do the job when this aid is not available.

Nuts and bolts that can be used again should be stored in a bucket of diesel oil to clean off the rust. Many old time fitters preferred using the same bolt again as it had been 'stretched', whereas a new bolt would require following up. Joints too,

Above: Few preserved railways have had full maintenance facilities from the start but one or two have been able to erect purpose-built workshops, including the Bluebell Railway. BR standard class 4 4-6-0 No 75027 is seen undergoing overhaul in Sheffield Park workshops during 1979. (*Bluebell Railway*)

Below: Where a wheel drop is not available a locomotive must be jacked up with jacks and packing in order to remove or replace wheels, as here at Buckfastleigh with BR standard 2-6-4T No 80064. (*J. R. Besley*)

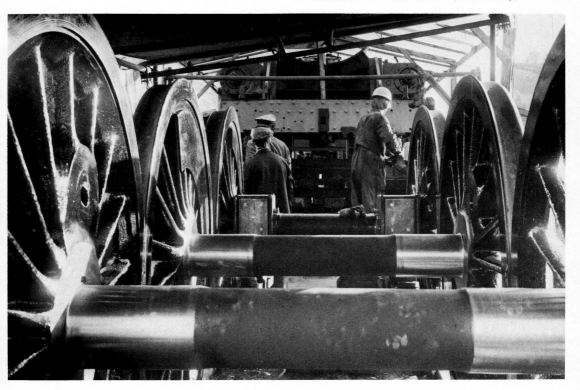

'ROBINSON' SUPERHEATER

Left: Fig 9. Diagram of the Robinson superheater showing the method of removing and expanding superheater elements.

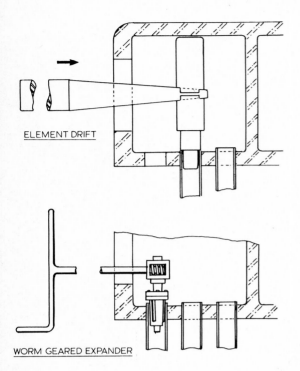

ELEMENT DRIFT

WORM GEARED EXPANDER

Right: Former Great Western 52XX 2-8-0T No 5239 recently restored, after about five years work, for the Dart Valley's Torbay line, a heavy engine but well needed on some of the peak 10 to 11 coach trains with 1 in 60 gradients.

should be hung on the smokebox door dart so that they are not lost.

Blanking plates of mild steel or plywood, cut to shape, should be bolted down to all apertures leading to the cylinders. It is not sufficient just to cover the opening with a piece of board, as this is apt to be kicked aside. Alternatively stuff a sack down each aperture. Meanwhile your mate, if you have one, can be usefully employed in running a die-nut down the numerous studs and bolts.

It is inevitable that in the course of time a stud will break or its threads become so corroded that it must be renewed. Nick it with a flat chisel, flush with the casting into which it is screwed and give it a few smart blows to and fro with a hammer in order to snap it off.

Now carefully centre punch the fractured surface of the stud exactly at its centre and proceed to drill it out with a drill slightly smaller than the root diameter of the thread.

When only an odd stud requires drilling out, the old fashioned hand ratchet, spade drill and drill post can be set up and the job done while a search is being made for that missing cable or faulty connection of an electric drilling machine.

The next task is to collapse the shell left by the drill. This is done by chipping a groove down it with a small slim round nose chisel known as a picking out tool. Great care must be taken not to damage the thread which is very easily done, especially in cast iron.

The thread should be cleaned up with a tap and a new stud screwed in with a stud box or two nuts locked one against the other; if the thread has gone too far it must be drilled out afresh to the tapping size for the next larger tap and a compound stud made and fitted. In other words if the stud in question is $\frac{3}{4}$ inch in diameter the end that screws into the casting must be $\frac{7}{8}$ inch diameter. It is not good practice merely to fit a larger stud and to enlarge the hole in the fitting, because first it introduces an odd size of nut and second because more often than not the larger nut cannot be got on through insufficient clearance.

The next job is to disconnect the superheater elements from the header. They may be either bolted to the header with or without a joint or expanded into it like a boiler tube, as in the case of

the Robinson superheater. Examples of the first kind are the original Schmidt and Swindon superheaters which use a copper joint or gasket. A modern development of the bolted type is the 'Melesco' ball ended element which makes metal to metal contact with a ground face. Plenty of perseverance and penetrating oil will be needed to unscrew the nuts securing these elements to the header.

Robinson expanded element

In the case of the Robinson expanded type, the inspection cover or covers on the header must be removed to gain access to the elements. Before attempting to drive out the elements from the header with the specially designed drift and wedge, it is most important that the protruding and enlarged end of the element is chipped off flush with the inside of the header. (See illustration for the special tools needed for extracting and replacing Robinson elements.)

Neglect of this elementary precaution by 'dilutee' labour during the second world war was responsible for many cracked and broken headers.

As a result of this damage, instructions were given that elements were to be burnt off and new ends welded on. This expense can be avoided, however, if proper care is taken in their extraction, as the same element can be re-expanded until the ends are either too thin or too short to be of further service. Only then should a new end become necessary. The ends, of course, should be annealed like a boiler tube.

MLS ball ended element

The Marine and Locomotive Superheater Co, the manufacturers of the 'Melesco' superheater, supply special cutters and hones for trueing up the ball ends of their elements and the conical seats in the header.

These tools, although a great convenience, are not a necessity unless pitting of the ball end is very deep. A simple and easily made successful alternative is a cup shaped lead lap (radius of cup $1\frac{1}{16}$ inch diameter of ball $2\frac{1}{8}$ inch) held in a carpenter's brace. A conical lap is also needed for grinding the seatings in the header. It is a slow process but gives good results.

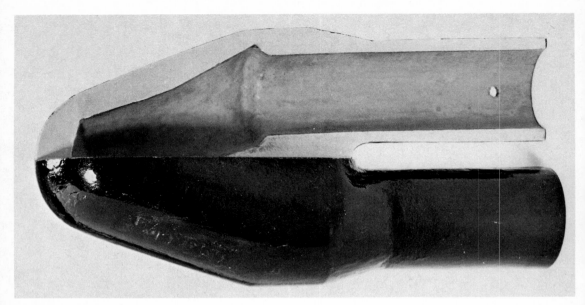

The spherical washers between the ball ends and bridge pieces must be thoroughly cleaned and ground in as well, with coarse carborundum, and all scale removed from the 'tee' head of the element securing bolt and its bearing place on the header. Failure to do this may result in leaking joints when expansion and contraction of the 'tee' bolt under heat crushes the scale separating these components and so loosens the joint.

Schmidt pattern element

It is false economy to re-use the old gaskets if new can be obtained but if not, they should be softened by heating to a cherry red and quenching in water.

Extraction of elements

If the superheater flues have been kept clean there should be little difficulty in pulling out the elements, but if they are stubborn the 'Pullift' is an ideal tool for this purpose. Try to attach the 'Pullift' to the spear end of the return loop rather than to the element legs, so that a direct pull is obtained. With the short return loop type there is no alternative to pulling on the legs which if bent or distorted will throw the joint faces out of square and cause endless trouble with leakage.

While the elements are out give them a thorough wire brushing and if coated with lime inside, rap them well with a wooden mallet in order to loosen the scale, which should be blown out or hosed out.

Finally test them hydraulically to at least 400 lb/square inch; a little detergent in the water will show up any pinholes by producing soap bubbles. As a temporary expedient these pinholes can be welded up with an oxy-acetylene torch, although renewal is advisable. Before replacing the elements see that the securing bands are not broken or corroded away; if so, new ones must be made.

Blast pipe

The carbon deposit inside the blast pipe should be burnt out by standing it on a couple of bricks and lighting a wood fire inside it.

Steam pipes

These should be tested for wastage by tapping with a light hammer; if they sound 'tinny' when struck and the vibration produced can be felt with the finger tips, they are too thin to be safe.

Thinning is usually quite local and occurs at ash level where the pipe is corroded by what is in effect dilute sulphuric acid. Wastage is usually made good by welding a sleeve round the affected area of the pipe and the advice of your boiler inspector should be sought on this point.

Copper steam pipes and their gunmetal elbows also wear thin and these are often repaired by brazing on a copper patch. All copper pipes should be softened before replacement by heating to a cherry red and quenching in cold water in order to destroy the brittleness caused by work

The torpedo end of a superheater element.
(*National Railway Museum*)

hardening. Take care not to burn a hole in the pipe; a green flame is an indication that the heat is too localised, so move the pipe to and fro in the fire and turn it from time to time. A properly annealed copper pipe has a salmon pink colour.

Superheater header

By this time the smokebox will have been completely stripped of all fittings except the superheater header. Occasionally a steam blow will develop between the header flange and the smokebox tube plate.

Remaking this joint is a major operation and engines developing this defect were usually sent to main works for attention; at times, though, it had to be done at a running shed and as more and more preservation centres are undertaking main works repairs, the method of tackling this task will be briefly described.

On many engines there is a panel in the smokebox wrapper plate behind the chimney, that can be removed to give access to the nuts securing the header to the tube plate; if there is not, one must be cut out neatly with a cutting torch (and subsequently welded back into position).

Owing to the cramped space, the nuts, which should have been well soaked with penetrating oil, are difficult to get at and cannot be split in the conventional way, it may however be possible to turn them with a hammer and a round nose chisel.

Before slackening the nuts, the header, weighing perhaps half a ton, must be supported by sliding two lengths of bullhead rail, each about six feet long, into two of the now empty flue tubes in the upper row. On these rails the superheater header, suitably packed, can be drawn back to gain access to the joint faces.

Great care was taken in the works to make this joint as perfect as possible by scraping both faces to a surface plate, using blue marking; as explained in 'Joint Making' the thinner the joint the better but before assuming that it is the joint that is at fault, examine closely the surface of the tube plate for a semi-circular fatigue fracture. This sometimes happens through long use and vibration caused by the header not being properly supported by the brackets riveted to the smokebox wrapper plate.

Air leaks

When the smokebox is empty take the opportunity to make good any air leaks that have been discovered. Engines with outside steam pipes are particularly prone to draw air where the pipe passes through the smokebox wrapper. There is usually an asbestos packed gland or seal of some kind at this point but few are wholly effective. A gap round the snifting valve is another weak point; this can be partially cured by a closely fitting cover plate.

Spark arrestors

When replacing the spark arresting screens in a self cleaning smokebox, make quite sure that they are securely fastened. A screen falling on top of the blast pipe can cause a dangerous blow back through the firehole.

CHIMNEY ALIGNMENT

Probably the greatest merit of the Stephenson locomotive boiler is its ability to produce automatically the power demanded from it. This is achieved by the ejector action of the steam blast up the chimney.

Within very wide limits it is true to say that the harder the engine is worked the fiercer is the blast. The greater the draught on the fire the more water is evaporated, producing more steam. All this is achieved by two simple, crude pieces of fixed equipment, the blast pipe and chimney. Although generally made of rough castings it is important that they should be axially in line and the correct distance apart. As more and more of our preserved locomotives will be needing new smokeboxes, it is as well to know how chimney alignment is achieved.

The blast pipe being mounted on a machined face on the cylinder or saddle casting is assumed to be true and the position of the chimney therefore is adjusted relative to the blast pipe orifice which in many instances has also a machined surface.

Proceed to level the engine with jacks and a spirit level placed on the footplating above the front buffer beam unless some other and more suitable position presents itself.

Now place the chimney in its approximate position on the smokebox and hang a plumb line across its diameter with the two weighted ends hanging down on each side of the chimney; then move the chimney until the distance between it

CHIMNEY ALIGNMENT

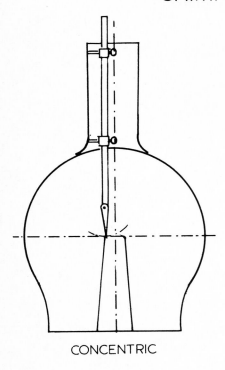

CONCENTRIC

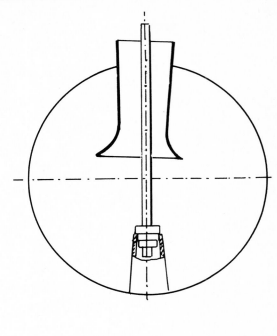

TILTED

and the plumb line measured with inside callipers is equidistant at each side.

Externally chimneys come in all sorts of shapes and sizes; internally they either taper outwards towards the top or are parallel. Obviously the taller the chimney the more accurately it can be set, conversely the shorter it is the less effect any slight misalignment will have.

A 'chimney stick' is now used to set the bore of the chimney in line with the blast orifice by means of an adjustable pointer that it has attached to its lower end. The chimney stick is tried in four positions round the chimney bore which we will designate North, South, East and West. First of all the fore and aft position of the chimney is equilised so that the pointer of the chimney stick just touches the rim of the blast orifice when the stick is moved from N to S without altering the pointer. The E to W position is adjusted in a similar manner.

Another and possibly better type of chimney stick, is one that aligns the chimney with the blast pipe axis as well as with its orifice. This consists of a length of new, straight boiler tube, mounted in a turned steel plug (stepped in such a way that it

will fit several sizes of orifice) that seats on the machined surface of the orifice. The chimney is set by equalising the distance between its bore and the tubular stick at choke and at its top.

It sometimes happens that the chimney is tilted in one direction or another and no matter how much it is moved about it cannot be centred with the blast orifice. In such a case drive small (fox) wedges between the wrapper plate and chimney base on the side towards which it leans until the tilt is corrected and the bore centred.

There are two ways of effecting a permanent adjustment, the Works method (or proper way), correcting the fault in the chimney by chipping or grinding off an equivalent amount of metal from its base at a point diametrically opposite to the wedges, or the other method by making and inserting a curved tapering liner equivalent in thickness to the wedges which it will replace.

On an old smokebox, before deciding that the chimney is at fault make sure that its wrapper plate has not wasted so thin that it is deflecting under the weight of the heavy chimney.

When the chimney has been correctly centred use it as a jig for drilling the holes in the wrapper

Fig 10. The use of a chimney stick to align a chimney concentrically above the blast pipe, described in the text below the diagram.

hammer thereby compressing the spring which may be either of steel or india-rubber.

Drawbars and pins should be annealed thoroughly by bringing them slowly to a red heat in a wood fire and allowing them to cool slowly in the fire as it dies out.

plate, then bolt down using a plastic filler such as is used for automobile repairs for stopping potential air leaks.

The 'tip to choke' measurement and blast orifice diameter can be checked if drawings are available but unless there is a considerable divergence from the designed dimensions any slight discrepancy is of no significance.

DRAW GEAR

The three principle methods of coupling an engine to its tender are:
1. By a spring loaded drawbar.
2. By a solid drawbar kept in tension by two powerful side buffers between engine and tender.
3. By a combination of both methods, popular on the Continent, where the buffing forces are taken by a large laminated spring, mounted horizontally in the tender dragbox to which the (spring) side buffers are attached.

The drawbar is connected to the spring at its centre, therefore the greater the pull the greater is the pressure on the side buffers which often terminate in inclined planes in order to exert a self centring action.

Uncoupling engine and tender

In order to uncouple Type 1 a large ring spanner (preferably with a ratchet) with a shank about four feet long is required. At its extremity is a shackle for attaching a rope to which a 'tug o'war' team apply their weight.

Type 2 is dealt with by securely scotching all the engine wheels and buffering up the tender with another engine. A tapped hole is provided in the main drawbar pin to enable it to be withdrawn with an eyebolt before the tender recoils. It is re-connected in the same way. The side buffers exert a pressure of six to seven tons.

Drawbar pins of Type 1 often terminate in a point. Advantage can be taken of this fact when re-coupling, by screwing up the drawbar nut until the point of the pin just enters the hole in the drawbar. It is then driven down with a big

SPRING CHANGING

Laminated bearing springs are of two types, those placed above the axlebox as on a tender, and those that are slung below, as are the majority of coupled axleboxes. The latter are particularly heavy and cumbersome to handle.

Taking as an example an inside cylinder six-coupled tank engine, on which it is intended to change a pair of underhung driving springs, the first step is to set the engine with the big ends on the top angles so that the hornstays and spring pins are accessible.

The next step is to pack between the frame and the top of the axle boxes that are to form the fulcrum for lifting but *not* to pack on top of the thin plate covering the oil well.

The third step is to place a 15 to 20 ton jack under each corner of the buffer beam at the end to be lifted or a single jack of 35 tons capacity at its centre.

When the springs have been relieved of weight, the 'tee' link pin connecting the spring to the axlebox can be knocked out. Sometimes this is masked by the hornstay, in which case, this too must be disconnected and dropped. The spring hanger adjusting nuts are not touched if it can be avoided.

When putting up the new springs this process is reversed, except that it may be necessary to place a jack under the spring buckle in order to align the holes in the spring 'tee' link. Individual springs are generally changed by this method as it saves jacking up the whole engine.

When no pit is available the work must be done on the level. After the old springs have been dragged clear and the new ones placed in position, a long bar thrust through the wheel from the outside can be used to raise the spring, in order that packing can be placed under it. This process is repeated until the spring is raised high enough to permit the spring hangers to be connected; the 'tee' link is then connected in the manner described above.

(continued on page 82)

The aims of preservationists can be summed up in this photograph showing the immaculate former Great Western 4-6-0 No 6000 *King George V*, with a train of preserved Great Western coaches belonging to the Severn Valley Railway/GW Society, leaving Newport, Gwent, on a special run to Shrewsbury on 3 July 1977. (*G. T. Heavyside*)

Before disturbing spring hanger adjusting nuts, measure either the amount the bolt protrudes or count the number of threads exposed, in order to ensure that the axle weights remain unaltered.

When doubt exists as to the wheel loading and 'Kelbus' portable weighing equipment is not available, a simple, although crude method is to place a two inch square of sheet lead in front of each wheel and then pull the engine over it; an increase in width and a decrease in thickness will indicate which wheel has the most weight.

FRAME STRAIGHTENING

When an engine is lifted off its wheels for major repairs, it is a good opportunity for checking the frames for alignment and horns for squareness.

The conventional plate framed steam locomotive is unique amongst steam machinery in possessing a flexible bed and a floating crankshaft, ideal features for negotiating a railway track with its frequent curves and changes in cross levels, but bad for the frame, by causing it to flex and fracture.

This occurs mainly between the cylinders and the driving axle at the corners of the horn gap and above the trailing bogie axle where the frame section is shallow and weak and is also subjected to repeated flexing by the traction forces.

Horns out of square are an indication that the frames are bent. This can be proved either with a long straight edge or by stretching a nylon line through the cylinder axis (see 'Slide Bar Alignment') to the most distant part of the frame and checking the distance between this and the frame with a pair of inside calipers.

Usually the bend is quite local and on the vertical axis. Mark this boldly in chalk on the *concave* side of the frame and then work up and down the depth of the frame with the ball peen of a riveting hammer, delivering a rain of rapid blows of moderate strength, as when riveting. The object of so doing is to compress and therefore expand the surface of the metal, which will 'come towards the hammer', just as the outside rail of a curve is longer than the inner.

Locomotives from the National collection are also being restored to or maintained in working order where possible, among them former LNWR 2-4-0 No 790 *Hardwicke*, built in 1873 and out of use for many years as a static museum exhibit. It is seen here piloting former Midland compound 4-4-0 No 1000 between Leeds and Shipley on a York–Carnforth run in 1976.
(*G. T. Heavyside*)

SECTION V
Accidents

DERAILMENTS

Accidents and breakdowns occur from time to time and these seem to be inseparable from railway work, occurring more often than not at inconvenient times and places, usually in the worst of weathers. The cause of many of these mishaps is failure of staff to obey operating rules or to establish a clear understanding with a colleague on the sequence of movements to be made.

Violent head-on collisions, vehicles projected over buffer stops, converging collisions at points or spectacular pile-ups on the main line are unlikely to occur at preservation centres but the odd derailment will undoubtedly occur sooner or later.

Derailment at points

The most common cause of derailment is facing points (not equipped with facing point locks) not properly closed, so permitting a wheel flange to pass between the switch blade and the stock rail and 'drop on the floor' as the gauge widens. Relaxation of pressure on the lever of spring points, thus allowing them to open, or a stone trapped between blade and stock rail can prevent the points from closing.

It is a well proved axiom amongst breakdown crews that the best way to re-rail a vehicle is to bring it back the way it went off.

In the case of a simple run off at facing points, where no other rails have to be surmounted, building a ramp of timber to raise the wheels to rail level and pulling on with another engine is the answer. If it is an engine that is derailed and it has steam, it is sometimes possible to use its own power to re-rail it, provided that every precaution is taken to ease the running-on process.

Time spent on constructing a solid and substantial ramp is amply repaid by the satisfaction of seeing each pair of wheels re-railed in rapid succession as the ramp is mounted. The importance of building a substantial ramp must be emphasised most strongly, especially where the distance between the switch blade and stock rail narrows, for it is here that the wheel, with an axle

load of perhaps 20 tons has to be raised high enough for the tread to roll on to the rail head. Short pieces of bull head rail, about 21 inches long that will span the distance between adjacent chairs, with a fish plate or two laid on top to gain sufficient height for the wheels to mount, make an admirable ramp. Failure to lift the wheels at this point will not only cause them to become firmly wedged as the rails converge, but may well burst the road.

Where short pieces of rail are not available, a firm bed on which to build a ramp of rail keys and fish plates must first be made by shovelling out ballast from between the sleepers and sliding in a thick piece of hardwood packing or short length of sleeper.

It is essential to remember the concentrated axle load that this ramp will have to sustain. All too often, wooden packing has been seen stuffed between the rails without adequate support, so that it is crushed under the weight of the advancing wheel and the track is damaged, without effecting re-railment. It is frequently found that the succeeding wheels have to climb over a cast iron chair that is immediately in front of them. In such a case it will pay to jack up the rear of the vehicle and build a timber ramp under the wheels, in order to ease the gradient to be climbed.

Whenever jacking, pack between the hornstay and the underneath of the axlebox so that no height is lost. Similarly, if the end pair of wheels are on the road and being used as a fulcrum when jacking up the opposite end, pack between the top of the axlebox and the frame with a large nut or iron packing of suitable thickness.

It will be found when pulling with another engine that a snatch with a slack coupling is far more effective at overcoming the initial resistance than a steady pull. If the derailed engine is 'down by the head' and its power is to be used to effect re-railment, do not overfill the boiler or priming will occur when it is restored to a level position.

Derailment on plain track

Fortunately, these are rare and occur generally on sharp curves. They are difficult to re-rail as the same lateral forces must be applied as caused the flange to climb the rail. Sometimes, the only remedy is to pull the engine back to a point where the curve is less severe and then re-rail with ramps.

Derailment where one or more rails have been crossed

Most often these are due to the speed or weight of the following vehicles pushing/pulling the derailed vehicle over several rails, often at a crossover. If it is not too badly off it can be re-railed with a traversing jack, but if it has to be moved several feet, it must be first jacked up and then lowered on to a substantial bed covered with well greased steel plates (old boiler plate) and skidded across with a winch or jack placed horizontally against the wheel.

Re-railing ramps

These are of two types, single and double. The 'Kelbus' heavy cast steel engine ramp is a good example of the former. These are made in pairs, LH inside and outside, RH inside and outside, and points, right and left. They are used as follows:

If the derailed wheels are off to the left of the rails in the direction in which pulling is to take place, then a pair of LH ramps is required, one for the inside of the rail and the other for the outside; if to the right, then a RH set is needed.

The special point ramps, if available, would obviate the necessity for packing between the switch blade and stock rail.

Double wing wagon ramps

These are not really suitable for re-railing heavy locomotives for they are too short, too obtuse and lack a shoulder to guide the wheel flange, as well as the rim which is the prime feature of the 'Kelbus' design. Whichever type of ramp is used it should be placed as close to the wheel as possible and well packed to prevent tilting.

Finally, there should be only one voice giving commands – that of the man in charge of the re-railing. Nothing is more confusing to the driver of the engine doing the pulling than to receive a barrage of conflicting orders. He should be first shown what is required and then told to ignore all commands except those of the man in charge.

Re-railment having been effected, wheels should be gauged and axle bearings and springs

It is vitally important that cranes, both fixed and rail-mounted, are inspected and maintained in accordance with regulations, and when in use that the operating limits are strictly observed. Only one person, the man in charge, should signal movements to the crane driver, as seen in the picture, *top right. Bottom right*: Close view of the Dart Valley 36 ton steam crane. Note the pointer denoting the angle of the jib. (*J. R. Besley, courtesy Dart Valley Railway*)

examined for damage or displacement. Track should also be examined, both to ascertain possible causes and for damage.

Unbraked vehicles

When moving an unbraked vehicle, such as a passenger coach or locomotive disconnected from its tender, with pinch bars on a gradient, have men with sprags and scotches ready to stop it running away. Scotches should be curved to suit the wheel (triangular chocks are apt to be pushed aside) and provided with a handle for easy and safe application.

CRANES

Lifting and hauling appliances and their tackle are subject to Statutory Rules and Orders governing their use and therefore come under the surveillance of the Railway Inspectorate. The following brief notes have been prepared for the guidance of those centres possessing either fixed or travelling cranes.

Testing of lifting appliances

Every crane and other hoisting machinery with its accessory gear shall be tested with a proof load which shall exceed the safe working load (swl) as follows:

SWL	Proof load
Up to 20 tons	25% in excess
20 to 50 tons	5 tons in excess
Over 50 tons	10% in excess
Chains	
Ring	
Hook	2 swl
Shackle	
Swivel	
Pulley blocks	4 swl
(Single sheave)	
Multiple blocks	
With swl up to 20 ton	2 swl
20 to 40 ton	20 ton in excess
Over 40 ton	$1\frac{1}{2}$ swl

Minimum size of chain to be used

Load to be lifted	Single leg sling	Subtended angle of a double leg sling		
		30°	90°	120°
Tons	Inches	Inches	Inches	Inches
$\frac{1}{2}$	$\frac{5}{16}$	$\frac{1}{4}$	$\frac{1}{4}$	$\frac{5}{16}$
1	$\frac{7}{16}$	$\frac{5}{16}$	$\frac{3}{8}$	$\frac{7}{16}$
2	$\frac{5}{8}$	$\frac{7}{16}$	$\frac{1}{2}$	$\frac{5}{8}$
3	$\frac{3}{4}$	$\frac{9}{16}$	$\frac{5}{8}$	$\frac{3}{4}$
5	$\frac{15}{16}$	$\frac{11}{16}$	$\frac{13}{16}$	$\frac{15}{16}$
10	$1\frac{5}{16}$	$\frac{15}{16}$	$1\frac{1}{8}$	$1\frac{5}{16}$
20	$1\frac{7}{8}$	$1\frac{5}{16}$	$1\frac{9}{16}$	$1\frac{7}{8}$

Annealing of chains, rings, hooks and shackles: $\frac{1}{2}$ inch and smaller every six months. All others every twelve months. (These periods are doubled for hand operated gear).

Wire ropes. Three monthly but if any wire is broken, to be examined monthly. 'No wire rope shall be used for hoisting or lowering, if in any length of eight diameters the total number of *visible* broken wires exceeds 10% of the total number of wires, or the rope shows signs of excessive wear, corrosion or other defect, which, in the opinion of the person who inspects it, renders it unfit for use.'

Single and double sling chains. The following examples have been selected to show the safe working load (swl) that any given size of chain will take.

It is most important to note the effect of spreading the hooks widely apart; the swl is *halved* when the legs of a double sling chain subtend an angle of 120°. *(See table above.)*

When in doubt as to the weight in working order of a locomotive or its tender, multiply the number of axles by the factor '16'. Exceptions to this generally applicable 'rule of thumb' are GW King 4-6-0s, LMS Coronation 4-6-2s, LNE V2s and the larger LMS tenders, where '18' is the appropriate factor. Coaches and wagons are always marked with their tare, or weight when empty.

Bridge spans and girders present a special problem. The weight of these may have to be estimated by detailed measurement and calculations, based on the thickness of the material used.

All authorised lifting tackle is stamped with its registered number and swl and users are required to record dates of annealing and testing of each piece of equipment in a Factories Act Register. Do not be tempted therefore to use other than registered and tested equipment, for in case of an accident involving injury to a human being, the consequences could be very grave.

Fixed cranes and hoists (power and hand). Of prime importance is an effective brake that will check and hold the heaviest weight that the crane will lift; this goes for all types of cranes whether fixed or travelling. Equally important on a hand operated crane is the pawl that prevents the load from dropping, it must work freely and engage properly with the teeth on the ratchet wheel. If the teeth of this and other highly loaded pinions are badly worn, the advice of a competent millwright should be sought.

Rail cranes

These can be hand or steam operated with either a fixed or a movable jib. Those with a movable jib will have attached to them near the hinge or pivot, an automatic load indicator, generally of the pendulum type, this indicates the swl that can be lifted at any given radius, both free on rail and when propped – that is with the outriggers extended and packed. It will be seen that in order to lift the greatest load of which the crane is capable, the jib must be raised to a nearly vertical position; conversely, when lowered to a nearly horizontal position, it can lift safely only a fraction of this weight. In other words, load and radius vary inversely as the following table inscribed on a 35 ton Ransome & Rapier crane will show.

Radius in feet	23	25	30	35
Load Free on rail	12	9	6	4½
(tons) Propped	35	30	25	18

A steam breakdown crane has its boiler, water tank and coal bunker mounted at the extremity of a platform extending to the rear of the crane, and this has attached to its underside, a heavy cast-iron counterweight in order to counterbalance the load being lifted. Unlike the jib which can be raised or lowered according to the load, the position of the counterweight is fixed.

This fact must always be kept in mind when slewing the crane free on rail without a load, especially on super-elevated track. Keep the jib well down in order to counterbalance the heavy tail weight and make the crane 'solid' by isolating the bearing springs with the screws or wedges provided for this purpose. More cranes have toppled over backwards when slewing round without a load than by tipping forward with an overload. The more powerful the crane and longer the jib, the greater is the risk of capsizing.

This does not or should not apply with the outriggers extended and packed, unless of course only those on the side facing the jib have been pulled out, for there is then nothing to stop the crane from toppling over backwards in the event of tackle breaking and the jib whipping upwards with the recoil.

Rail clips are provided and should be applied always whether the crane is free on rail or propped. They should be left slack so that in the event of the crane wheels starting to unload they will tighten and betray this fact to the groundman (who should always be stationed behind the crane) and who will warn the man in charge and

the crane driver when the wheels start to lift clear of the rail.

When packing the outriggers the nature of the ground should be considered.

Type of ground	Safe bearing
Made ground	2 tons/square foot
Soft clay	4 tons/square foot
Gravel	15 tons/square foot
Chalk	25 tons/square foot

If the ground does not feel solid when stamped upon, spread the load by placing two sleepers side by side on the ground, before building up the packing, which should be of hard wood.

It is a wise precaution before attempting to lift in earnest, to compress the packing (and the ground under it), by first raising the load just clear of the ground and lowering it again and then re-tightening the jack screws or in some designs, wedges.

If you are faced with an overload, make a head-on lift with the jib straight up if you can. A Britannia Pacific weighing 94 tons has been lifted at the front end by a 35 ton Ransome crane without the slightest difficulty.

If you have to travel with a heavy load, do so with it as near the ground as possible, preferably in front of the crane or resting against its side. If anything untoward should happen it has not far to fall and the crane will remain on the rails.

Do not forget to raise the screws or remove the wedges from the springs before normal travel is resumed, otherwise a derailment or hot box will occur. Above all, tell the crane driver to ignore all orders except those of the person in charge.

When lifting or pulling operations are in progress, warn everyone in the immediate vicinity to stand well clear, especially when snatching, or else they may be injured by flying ropes or broken chains in the event of tackle breaking, nor should anyone be allowed to stand under a suspended load.

Random Data and Rules of Thumb

An express locomotive hauling a 400 ton train will consume roughly 45 lb of coal, 35 gall of water per mile at high power output or 40 lb of coal, 30 gall of water per mile at moderate power output.

A superheated engine will evaporate 8 lb of water per 1 lb of coal. A saturated engine will evaporate 10 lb of water per 1 lb of coal.

Oil consumption per 100 miles
Small engine   1 pint cylinder oil 4 pints axle oil
Large engine   2 pints cylinder oil 8 pints axle oil

Coal   *Best Medium Low*
(calorific value BTU)   14 to 15 12 to 13 10 to 11
per lb x 000
Volume 43cu ft per ton, or a 3ft 6in cube
Water 1 gall weighs 10 lb
         1cu ft weighs 62.4 lb
         1cu ft contains 6.24 gall
         Hydraulic head $\frac{1}{2}$ lb/sq in per foot

Smokebox vacuum 1 inch of water for each pound of blast pipe pressure. *Time to raise steam* from cold, without forcing, 3 or 5 hours. Full pressure within 30 to 40 minutes of steam showing at the whistle.

Vacuum brake working at a vacuum of 21 inches of mercury is equivalent to a pressure of 10 lb/sq in acting on the piston.

Temperatures (approx.) firebox 2,000°F, smokebox 500°F = boiler heat absorbtion efficiency of 75%.

Water freezing into ice expands $\frac{1}{11}$ of its volume hence the desirability of draining lubricator and injectors in frosty weather.

Mild steel has a tensile strength of 28 to 32 ton per sq in section. A 1 inch diameter steel bolt will carry a load of 6 tons safely. (2p piece = 1 inch diameter).

Pitch of firebox stays. 4 inches below 150 lb/sq in, $3\frac{1}{2}$ inches above.

Hydraulic test $1\frac{1}{2}$ times working pressure, all caulking to be done below 60 lb/sq in.

Spring deflection. Bearing springs, $\frac{1}{4}$ inch per ton.

Whitworth nuts. Distance across flats = $1\frac{1}{2}$ dia + $\frac{1}{8}$ inch.

Approximate Weight in Working order of locomotives and tenders

Majority	Number of axles x '16'=Tons
GW 'King'	
LMS 'Coronation	Number of axles x
LNE V2	'18'=Tons
LMS larger tenders	

Adhesion factor		*Conditions*
Best	25%	Very dry rail, very wet rail.
Normal	20%	
Worst	10% or less	Rail greasy, through fog, falling snow or frost.

Bronze bushes

	Nominal Diameter (Inches)				
	2	3	5	7	10
Press fit	2.003	3.004	5.005	7.006	10.007

Allow $\frac{1}{64}$ inch extra in bore for closing in.

Running clearance. One thou per inch diameter.

Metric equivalents
Abbreviation

Weight	Imperial	Metric
oz	Ounce	28·35 Grammes
lb	Pound	0·4536 Kilogrammes
cwt	Hundredweight (1/20 ton)	50·8 Kilogrammes
Ton	Ton (2240 lb)	1016·0 Kilogrammes

Pressure
PSI or lb/sq in = Pounds per square inch
14·7 psi = 1 Atmosphere
Tons/sq ft = Tons per square foot
Tonnes/sq metre = Tons/sq ft × 10·96

POUNDS PER SQUARE INCH IN KILOGRAMMES
PER SQUARE CENTIMETRE

1	0·0703	70	4·9215	225	15·8191
5	0·3515	80	5·6246	250	17·5767
10	0·7031	90	6·3276	275	19·3344
20	1·4062	100	7·0307	300	21·0921
30	2·1092	125	8·7884	325	22·8496
40	2·8123	150	10·5460	350	24·6073
50	3·5153	175	12·3037	375	26·3650
60	4·2184	200	14·0614	400	28·1227

Length
'Thou' One thousandth part
of an inch   0·0254mm
$\frac{1}{64}$ inch   0·396mm
$\frac{1}{32}$ inch   0·793mm
$\frac{1}{16}$ inch   1·587mm
$\frac{1}{8}$ inch   3·175mm
$\frac{1}{4}$ inch   6·35mm

Volume (Liquid)
Gall   Gallon   4·546 Litres

Temperature
°F   Degrees Fahrenheit 32°F=0°C (Celsius)
                                              212°F=100°C

Consumption
lb/mile Pounds per mile   0·2818 Kg/Kilometre
BTU   British
             Thermal Unit   0·252 Calorie

Other abbreviations used in this book

BR   British Railways
GER   Great Eastern Railway
GWR   Great Western Railway
LB&SCR   London, Brighton & South Coast
                 Railway
LMS   London, Midland & Scottish Railway
LNER   London & North Eastern Railway
LTSR   London, Tilbury & Southend Railway
NER   North Eastern Railway
SR   Southern Railway

swl   safe working load
swg   steel wire gauge

A number of Continental European locomotives have been preserved in Britain bringing, in some cases, different types of fittings and equipment from those on British locomotives, different graduations of, for example, boiler pressures and usually other standards for components, nuts, bolts etc. This is a Swedish 2-6-2T preserved on the Nene Valley Railway near Peterborough. (*G. T. Heavyside*)

Simple Translation of Comparative Terms

ENGLISH		FRENCH	GERMAN
UK	USA		
Boiler	——	Chaudière	Kessel
Barrel	——	Corps Cylindrique	Langkessel
Tubes	——	Tubes	Rauchrohren
Superheater flue	——	Gros tube à fumée	Heizrohr
Superheater element	——	Element surchauffeur	Uberhitzerrohrsatz
Smokebox tube plate	Front tube sheet	Plaque tubulaire de bôite à fumée	Rauchkammerrohrwand
Firebox	Boiler back head	Bôite à feu	Hinterkessel
Inner firebox	——	Foyer	Feuerbüchse
Firebox tube plate	Back tube sheet	Plaque tubulaire	Feuerbüchsrohrwand
Firebox door plate	Door sheet	——	Feuerbüchsrückwand
Firebox crown plate	Roof sheet	Ciel du foyer	Feuerbüchsmantel
Firebox side stay	Stay bolt	Entretoise	Stehbolzen
Firebox roof stay	Radial stay	Tirant de ciel du foyer	Deckenstehbolzen
Longitudinal stay	Back head brace	Tirants longitudinaux	Stehkessel
	Front tube sheet brace		
Palm stay	——	Agrafes	Bodenanker
Firebox girder bars	——	Fermes longitudinal	——
Foundation ring	——	Cadre	Bodenring
Dome	——	Dôme	Dom
Mud hole door	Washout hole	Tampon autoclave	Waschluke
Washout plug	——	Bouchon de lavage	Reinigungschrauben
Grate	——	Grille	Rost
Firebars	——	Barreaux de grille	Roststäbe
Drop grate	——	——	Kipprost
Rocking grate	——	Grille à secousses	——
Ashpan	——	Cendrier	Aschkasten
Damper door	——	Porte de cendrier	Klappen
Arch tubes	——	Tubes à eau	——
Thermic syphon	——	Siphon 'Nicholson'	——
Brick arch	——	Voûte en briques	Feuerschirm
Air deflector plate	——	Deflecteur d'air	——
Mouthpiece protection plate	——	——	——
Firedoor	——	Porte du foyer	Feuertür
Smokebox	——	Bóite à fumée	Rauchkammer
Smokebox door	——	Porte de bôite à fumée	Rauchkammertür
Superheater header	——	Surchauffeur	Überhitzer
Superheater snifting valve	——	Soupape de rentrée d'air	
Chimney	Smokestack	Cheminée	Schornstein
Blast pipe	Exhaust pipe	Échappement	Blasrohr
Steam pipes	——	Tuyau de prise de vapeur	Dampfeinströmrohr
Blower ring	——	Souffleur annulaire	Hilfsbläser

in Various Languages

POLISH	PORTUGUESE	S.A. SPANISH
Kotla	Caldeira	Caldera
Walczak	Corpo de bomba: corpo cilíndrilo de caldeira	Cuerpo cilíndrico
Plomieniówki	Tubos; canos	Tubos chicos
Plomience	Condutos, tubos do superaquecedor; fumeiros	Tubos grandes
Elementy przegrzewacza	Elementos do superaquecedor	Elementos del sobrecalentador
Ściana sitowa walczka	Chapa tubular da caixa de fumo	Placa tubular delantera
Stojak	Caixa de fogo	Caja de fuego exterior/envolente
——	Caixa de fogo; camara de combustão; fornalha	Caja de fuego/hogar
Ściana sitowa skrzyni ogniowej	Chapa de tubos; chapa tubular (de caixa de fogo)	Placa tubular trasera
Ściana drzwiczkowa skrzyni ogniowej	Crapa de porta (de caixa de fogo)	Placa posterior del hogar
Podniebiene	Chapa de cobertura (de caixa de fogo)	Cielo del hogar
Zespórka	Esteois laterais	Estays/virotillos laterales
Zespórka podniebiene	Esteios superiores, ou de cobertura	Tirantes
Ściagi podluzni	Esteios longitudinais	——
Sciagi sciany drzwiczkowej stojaka		
Sciag ściany sitowej	Esteios de pata; de garra	Palme estays
——	Longarinas da caixa de fogo; da câmara de combustão	Puentes
Wieniec stopowy	Aro da caixa de fogo	Marco fundamental de la caja de fuego
Zbieralnik pary	Domo; cúpula	Domo
Wyczystka	Porta de residual: de limpeza	Tapa autoclave
Korek wyczstkowy	Bujão de vaziamento; extração; limpeza	Tapon de lavaje
Ruszt	Grelha	Parrilla
Rusztowine	Barras de grelha	Grillas
Rusztwywrotna	Porta pendente; comporta corrediça	Parrilla volcable
Ruszt wstrzą sany	Grelha osclante; de oscillação	Grilla móvil
Popielnik	Aparador de cinza	Cenicero
Klapa przednia	Amortecedor; abafador; registo	Grampà/registro
Rury cyrkulacyjne	Esteios tubulares em arco' tubos para arcos	Tubos termosifones
——	Sifão térmico	Termo sifón
Sklepienie paleniskowe	Arco de tijolos	Boveda
——	Defletor de ar	Deflector
——	Bocal protetor; de proteção	Protector de la boga del hogar
Drzwiczki paleniskowe	Porta de fogo; de fornalha	Puerta del hogar
Dymnica	Caixa de fumaça (ou fumo)	Caja de humos
Drzwy dymnicy	Porta da caixa de fumaça (ou fumo)	Puerta de la caja de humos
Skrzynia przegrzewacza	Coletor do superaquecedor; cabaçote	Caja colectora
	Válvula de aspiração do superaquecedor	Välvula atmosférica
Komin	Chaminé	Chimenea
Dysza wylotowa	Tubo de pressão; de jato; explosão ou imflamação; de injeçao do ar de combustão; de fole; colona de escape; de descarga	Boquilla de escape
Rura wlotowa	Tubos (ou condutores) de vapor	Caňos de admision
Dmuchawka parowa	Ventilador annular	Corona del soplador

ENGLISH UK	ENGLISH USA	FRENCH	GERMAN
Blower valve	——	Soupape de souffleur	Hilfbläserventil
Spark arrestor	Netting basket	Grille à flammèches	Funkenfänger
Regulator valve	Throttle valve	Régulateur	Regler
Safety valve	——	Soupape de sûreté	Kesselsicherheitsventil
Fusible plug	——	Bouchon fusible	Schmelzpfropfen
Water gauge	Water gage	Tube de niveau	Wasserstandanzeiger
Pressure gauge	Pressure gage	Manomètre	Druckmesser
Whistle	——	Sifflet	Dampfpfeife
Injector	Inspirator	Injecteur	Dampfstrahlpumpe
Lifting injector	——	Injecteur aspirant	Saugendepumpe
Non lifting injector	——	Injecteur non-aspirant	Nicht saugendepumpe
Exhaust injector	——	Injecteur à vapeur d'èchappement	Abdampfstrahlpumpe
Clack valve	Boiler check valve	Chapelle d'introduction d'eau	Rückschlagventil
Steam valve	——	Soupape de prise de vapeur	Dampfabsperrventil
Plug cock	——	Robinet	Hahn
Overflow valve	——	Soupape de trop plein	Schlabberventil
Overflow pipe	——	Trop plein	Überlauf
Delivery pipe	——	Tuyau de refoulement	Speiseleitung
Feed pipe	——	Tuyau d'arrivée d'eau	Saugleitung
Engine	——	Machine	Maschine
Tender engine	——	Machine tender	Lok mit Schleptender
Tank engine	——		Tender lokomotive
Cylinder	——	Cylindre	Zylinder
Cylinder cover	——	Plateau du cylindre	Zylinderdeckel
Cylinder drain cock	——	Purgeurs	Zylinder ventil
Cylinder pressure relief valve	——	Soupape de décharge	Zylindersicherheitsventil
Piston	——	Piston	Kolben
Piston rod	——	Tige du piston	Kolbenstange
Piston rings	——	Bague du piston	Kolbenringe
Piston gland	——	Garniture	Kolbenstangestopfbuchse
Asbestos packing	——	——	——
Metallic packing	——	Garniture metallique	——
Cast iron packing	——	Garniture en fonte	Gusseisennen dichtring
Steam chest	Valve chamber	Bôite à vapeur	Schieberkasten
Port face	——	Table des lumières	Schieberspiegel
Steam port	——	Lumières d'admission	Dampfkanal
Exhaust port	——	Lumière de'échappement	Ausströmleitung
Lap	——	Recouvrement exteriéur	Einströmuberdeckung
Lead	——	Avance linéaire	Lineares voreilen
Slide valve	——	Tiroir plan	Flachschieber
Valve buckle	Valve yoke	——	——
Valve spindle	Valve stem	Tige de tiroir	Schieberstange
Piston valve liner or sleeve	Valve bushing	Chemise de tiroir	Schieberbuchse
Piston valve	——	Tiroir cylindrique	Kolbenschieber
Outside admission	——	Admission extérieure	Äusserer Einströmung
Inside admission	——	Admission intérieure	Innere Einströmung
Slide bars	Crosshead guides	Glissières	Gleitbahn
Crosshead	——	Tête ou crosse de piston	Kreuzkopf
Gudgeon pin	Wrist pin	Tourillon	Kreuzkopfbolzen
Connecting rod	Main rod	Bielle motrice	Treibstange
Coupling rod	Side rod	Bielle d'accouplement	Kuppelstange
Crank pin	——	Manivelle	Zapfen
Crank axle	——	Essieu coudé	Gekröpften Achswelle
Big end	——	Gros tête de bielle motrice	Treibstangen köpfe
Bushed		Gros tête à bague	——

POLISH	PORTUGUESE	S.A. SPANISH
———	Válvular insufladora; exhaustora; de ventilação; de insuflação; de exhaustão	Válvular del soplador
Odiskiernik	Pára-faíscas; faúlheiro	Chispera
Zawór przepustnica	Válvula reguladora	Regulador
Zawór bezpieczénstwa	Válvula de segurança	Válvular de seguridad
Korki topliwe	Bujão cápsula-fusível	Tapon fusible
Wodowskaz rurkowy	Indicador, ou manômetro, de nível de água	Nivel
Manometre	Manômetro, aferidor, indicador de pressão	Manómetro
Gwizdawka parowa	Apito; apito de alarme ou aviso	Pito/silbato
Inżectory	Injetor	Inyector
Inżector ssaço-tłoçzacy	Vapor atiyo de injetor (de elevaçao)	Inyector aspirante
Inżector tłoçsacy	Vapor ativo de injetor (não elevador)	Inyector
Inżector na pare odlotowa	Vapor de descarga ou expusão, de injetor	Inyector a vapor de escape
Zawór zwrotny	Válvula de charneira	Valvula de introducción
Zawór parowy	Válvula de vapor	Válvula de vapor
Kurki	Torneira ou rolinete, de macho ou de ponteiro	Macho de paso de agua
Zawór przelewowy	Válvula de extravazamento, ou de transborde	Válvular de rebosadero
Rury przelewowa	Tubo extravazamento, de transborde	Caño rebosadero
Przewód tloczny	Tubo, cano de pressão, de descarga, de distribuição do injetor	Caño de introduccion
Rura doplywu wody z tendra	Tubo, cano, conduto de alimentação	Caño de introduccion
Parowóz	Motor	Máquina
———	Motor tender	Mácquina con ténder
Tendrzak	Motor tanque, depósito, reservatório	Mácquina tanque
Cylinder	Cilindro	Cilindro
Pokrywa cylindrowe	Tampa, cobertura do cilindro	Tapa de cylindro
Zawór przedmuchowy	Torneira de purgação, de drenagem – do cilindro	Purgador
Zawór bezpieczeństwa	Válvula de alivio de pressão	Valvular de seguridad de cilindro
Tlok	Pistão	Piston
Trzon tlokowy	Biela, braço, tirante do pistão	Vástago
Pierścené tlokowy	Aneis de segmento do pistão	Aros
Dlawnica cylindrowa	Sobeposta da haste do êmbolo, do pistão	Prensaestopas
Dlawnica ze szczeliwem miekkim	Guarnição, empanque do pistão (amianto asbesto)	Empaquetadura de amianto
	Guarnição, empanque do pisão (metal)	Empaquetadura de metal blanco
Pierścieńuszeeiniające	Guarnição, empanque do pistão (ferro fundido)	Empaquetadura con/elementos de fundición
Skrzynia suwakowa	Caixa de distribuição, ou distribuidora	Caja de valvula
———	Espelho do distribuidor	———
Kanaly parowe	Orifíco de admissão de vapor	Lumbrera
Kanal odlotowy	Orifíco, bocal de escapamento, de descarga	Lumbrera de escape
Przyslloniecie wlotu	Recobertura; recobrimento; sobriposição	Recubrimiento
Linijnym wyprzedzeniem	Avanço linear	Avance a la admisión
Suwak plaski	Válvula de corrediça	Válvula plana
———	Fivela, braçadeira, cinto da válvular	Marco
———	Haste, fuso da válvula	Vástago
Tuleja suwakowa	Válvula do pistão' êmbolo distribuidor camisa/manga	Camisa de válvula
Suwak okrągly	Válvula do pistão	Valvula cilindrica
Zewnetrznego doplywu pary	Amissão externa (vályula do pistão)	Válvula cilindrica de admisión externa
Przywewnetrznym doplywie pary	Amissão interna (válvula do pistão)	Válvula cilindrica de admisión interna
Prowadnica krzyżulca	Barras corrediças; deslizantes; diretrizes; paralelas	1, Guia de corredera. 2, Paralelas
Krzyżulec	Cruzeta; travessa superior	Cruceta
	Pino da cruzeta	Perno de punta chica
Korbowód	Haste de ligaçao; de articulaçao	Biela motriz
Wiązary	Vareta de união; barra de acoplamento; braço conetor	Biela acoplante
Czopy korbowe	Pino de manivela' munhaõ ou moente, perno da biela; munhão do vira brequim	Muñon
Osie wykorbione	Eixo de manivela	Cigüeñal
	Cabeça de puxavante; de biela de tirante	Punta grande
	De buxa, chumaceira	a buje

ENGLISH UK	ENGLISH USA	FRENCH	GERMAN
Strapped	——	Gros tête à chape rapportée	Schnallen köpfe
Marine	——	Gros tête à chape rapportée et écrous filetée	——
Stephenson's valve gear	——	Distribution Stephenson	Stephenson Steuerung
Eccentric sheave (Fore)	——	Poulie d'eccentrique (Avant)	Hubschiebe (Vorwärts)
Eccentric sheave (Back)	——	Poulie d'eccentrique (Arrière)	Hubschiebe (Rückwärts)
Eccentric rod (Fore)	——	Barre d'eccentrique (Avant)	Schwingenstange (Vorwärts)
Eccentric rod (Back)	——	Barre d'eccentrique (Arrière)	Schwingenstange (Rückwärts)
Eccentric strap	——	Collier d'eccentrique	Hubscheibenring
Expansion link	Reverse link	Coulisse de distribution	Schwinge
Expansion link die block	Reverse link block	Coulisseau	Schwingenstein
Reversing rod	Reach rod	Barre de changement de marche	Steuerstange
Walschaert's valve gear	——	Distribution Walschaerts	Heusinger Steurung
Return crank	Eccentric crank	Contre-manivelle	Gegenkurbel
Eccentric rod	——	Bielle de commande de coulisse	Schwingenstange
Radius rod	——	Bielle de commande du tiroir	Schieberschubstange
Combination lever	——	Levier d'avance	Voreil hebel
Union link	Crosshead link	Bielle de commande de levier d'avance	Lenkerstange
Crosshead arm	——	Levier de commande de levier d'avance	Lenkenansatz am Kreuzkopf
Wheel	——	Roue	Rad
Tyre	Tire	Bandage	Radreifen
Axle	——	Essieu	Achsen
Bogie	Truck	Bogie	Drehgestell
Axlebox	Journal box	Bôite motrice	Achslager
Axlebox keep	Journal box cellar	Dessous de bôite	Achslagerunterkasten
Horn block/cheek	Pedistal	Plaque de garde	Achslagerfuhrung
Hornstay	Pedistal tie	Entretoise	Achsgabelsteg
Axlebox wedge	Driving box wedge	Coins de rattrapace de jeu	Achslagerstelkeil
Bearing spring	——	Ressort du suspension	Tragfeder
Plate frame	——	Longeron en tôle	Blechrahmenwange
Bar frame	——	Longeron en barre	Barrenrahmen
Buffer	——	Tampon	Puffer
Drawgear	——	Attelage	Kupplung
Screw coupling	——	Tendeur à vis	Schrauben kupplung
Westinghouse brake	——	Frein Westinghouse	Druckluftbremse
Air pump	——	Pompe	Luftpumpe
Driver's valve	Engineer's brake valve	Robinet de mécanicien	Führerbremsventil
Triple valve	——	Triple valve	Steuerventil
Brake pipe	——	Conduite générale	Hauptluftleitung
Brake cylinder	——	Cylindre de frein	Bremszylinder
Brake block	Brake shoe	Sabôt	Bremsklotz
Lubricators	——	Graisseur	——
Sight feed	——	Graisseur à condensation	——
Mechanical	——	Graisseur mécanique	Schmierpumpe
Syphon	——	Graisseur à mèche	——
Pin trimming	——	Graisseur à épinglette	Stangenlager Schmiergefä

POLISH	PORTUGUESE	S.A. SPANISH
Lby korbowodów dzielone	De cinta	Con counete partido
Korbowód z lbem dzielonym	Marítima	——
Stawidlo	Distribuição, mecanismo de vávulas – Stephenson	Distribucion Stephenson
Mimósród (naprzod)	Roldana/polia excêntrica (anterior)	Excéntrica de marcha adelante
Mimósród (do tylu)	Roldana/polia excêntrica (posterior)	Excéntrica de marcha atrós
——	Vara, vareta, tirant excêntrica (anterior)	Biela excéntrica de marcha adelante
——	Vara, vareta, tirant excêntrica (posterior)	Biela excéntrica de marcha atrós
——	Cinta, braçadeira excêntrica	Collar de la excentrica
Jarzmo	Articulação, braço biela de expansão, dilatăao	Sector
——	Matriz da articulação, da biela, do braço de expansão dilatação	Dado
Drazek	Alavanca de rerversão, inversão de marcha, de contre-marcha	Barra de cambio de marcha
Stawidla Walschaerta	Engrenagem, mecanismo de válvulas-Walschaert	Distribucion Walschaert
Przecikorba	Contre-manivela, manivela de retrocesso	Excéntrica
Wadzidlo jarzma	Vara, vareta, biela, tirante-excêntricos	Biela excéntrica
Wodzidlo suwaka	Vara, vareta, biela, tirante-radial, de raio	Biela radial
Wahacz	Alavanca de combinação; pendural de avanço	Biela de avance
Wodzidlo wahacza	Biela de união, de avanço	Eslabón
——	Braço, ou palmatória da cruzeta	Pié del eslabón
Zestawy kolowe	Bandagem de roda' roda de propulsão; aro de aço	Ruedas (cubo, rayos, corona)
Przekroj	Bandagem de roda	Llanta
Os parowozowa	Eixo; ávore; rodeiro	Eje
Wózek dwuosiowy	Truque; vagão de trayessa giratória	Bogie
Lożyska osiowe	Caixa da graxa ou do jôgo	Caja (de eje)
Spodek maznicy	Parte inferior da caixa de eixo	Contra caja
Oprawa wykroju ostojnicy blachowej Prowadnice w wykroju ostojnicy belcowej	Armação de pedistal; cavalete; terminal	Guia de la caja/frente de la caja
Zwora	Esteio de pedistal; de cavalette; de terminal	Atăguia
Klin	Cunha da caixa de eixo	Cuňa
Sprezyny nosne (resory)	Mola de suporte	Elástico
Ostoja	Armação de chàpa, ou de placa; quadro de chapa ou de placa, longerão	Bastidor de chapa
Ostojnica belkowa	Armação de barra; longerina lateral	Bastidor de barras
Zderzak	Tampão; amortecedor: pára-choques	Paragolpes
Polaczenie tendre z parowozem	Engate; tirante	Enganche
Sprzęg śrubowy	Engate de parafuso, ou de rôsca	Enganche a tornillo
Urzadzenia hamulcowy	Freio; breque; travão (Westinghouse)	Freno de aire comprimido
Sprężárka	Bomba de ar	Compresor
Zawór maszynisty	Válvula de conducão; de transmissão: de propulsão	Llave del maquinista
Zawór rozrzadezy	Válvula tripla: ou trifásica	Triple valvula
Przewód glowny	Tubo de breque: travagem	Cañeria de freno
Cylinder hamulcowy	Cilindro de frenagem	Cilindro de freno
Klocka hamulcowego	Calço do eixo do freio	Zapata de freno
——	Lubrificadores	Lubricador
——	De alimentacão ou passagem visivel; de mira ou visor	Hidrostatico
Pompy olejowe	P. mecânica	Bomba de aceite
——	Alimentaçao de sifão	Mecha
——	Alimentaçao de equilíbrio ou compenssacão de pino ou perno	Aguja

Bibliography
(Not all titles are still in print but might be available at libraries).

'Some Suggestions on Maintenance Schedules for the Guidance of Minor and Light Railways, Operating Steam Locomotives', A. G. W. Garraway MBE, Association of Railway Preservation Societies Information Sheet No. 27

Handbook for Railway Steam Locomotive Enginemen (BR33014), British Transport Commission.

Locomotive Management from Cleaning to Driving, Jas. T. Hodgson MIMechE and John Williams, The Railway Engineer.

Steam Locomotive Design: Data and Formulae, E. A. Phillipson AMInstCE, AMIMechE, MILocoE, The Locomotive Publishing Company.

Locomotive Cyclopedia, Simmons Boardman, USA.

La Machine Locomotive, E. Sauvage and A. Chapelon, Beranger.

Leitfaden für den Dampflokomotivdienst, L. Niederstrasser, Reinhold Rudolph.

Valves and Valve Mechanisms, Professor W. Dalby.

Locomotive Valves and Valve Gears, Yoder and Wharen, Van Nostrand.

La Locomotive Actuelle a Vapeur, E. Devernay, Dunod.

The Steam Engine and other Heat Engines, J. A. Ewing, Cambridge University Press.

Locomotive Engineers' Pocket Book, The Locomotive Publishing Company.

Mechanical World Year Book, Mechanical World Office.

Molesworth's Pocket Book of Engineering Formulae, Sir Guilford Molesworth KCIE, E. & F. N. Spon Ltd.

'The Influence of the Treatment of Boiler Waters on the Maintenance and Utilisation of Steam Locomotives', M. Louis Armand, *Proc. Inst. of Loco. E. Vol. 230.*

An immaculate *Green Arrow*, with the author undertaking inspection at Carnforth in 1973, ready for a main line run. Notice the typical Harvey touches of burnished smokebox door hinges, frame edges, buffers and guard-irons. (*London Midland Region, BR*)